WORKING
WITH PLASTICS

FITNESS, HEALTH & NUTRITION
HEALTHY HOME COOKING
UNDERSTANDING COMPUTERS
THE ENCHANTED WORLD
LIBRARY OF NATIONS
HOME REPAIR AND IMPROVEMENT
CLASSICS OF EXPLORATION
PLANET EARTH
PEOPLES OF THE WILD
THE EPIC OF FLIGHT
THE SEAFARERS
WORLD WAR II
THE GOOD COOK
THE TIME-LIFE ENCYCLOPAEDIA OF GARDENING
THE GREAT CITIES
THE OLD WEST
THE WORLD'S WILD PLACES
THE EMERGENCE OF MAN
LIFE LIBRARY OF PHOTOGRAPHY
TIME-LIFE LIBRARY OF ART
GREAT AGES OF MAN
LIFE SCIENCE LIBRARY
LIFE NATURE LIBRARY
THE TIME-LIFE BOOK OF BOATING
TECHNIQUES OF PHOTOGRAPHY
LIFE AT WAR
LIFE GOES TO THE MOVIES
BEST OF LIFE
LIFE IN SPACE

This volume is part of a series offering home
owners detailed instructions on repairs,
construction and improvements which they can
undertake themselves.

HOME REPAIR
AND IMPROVEMENT

WORKING WITH PLASTICS

BY THE EDITORS OF
TIME-LIFE BOOKS

TIME-LIFE BOOKS
AMSTERDAM

TIME-LIFE BOOKS

EUROPEAN EDITOR: Kit van Tulleken
Assistant European Editor: Gillian Moore
Design Director: Ed Skyner
Chief of Research: Vanessa Kramer
Chief Sub-Editor: Ilse Gray

HOME REPAIR AND IMPROVEMENT

EDITORIAL STAFF FOR WORKING WITH PLASTICS
Editor: Robert M. Jones
Senior Editor: Betsy Frankel
Designer: Edward Frank
Text Editors: Victoria W. Monks, Brooke Stoddard
(principals), Rachel Cox, Peter Pocock, Mark M. Steele
Writers: Tim Appenzeller, Kevin Armstrong, Carol
Jane Corner, Stuart Gannes, Kathy Kiely, Kirk Y.
Saunders
Art Assistants: George Bell, Fred Holz, Lorraine D.
Rivard, Peter Simmons
Picture Co-ordinator: Betsy Donahue
Editorial Assistant: Cathy A. Sharpe

EUROPEAN EDITION
Series Director: Charles Boyle
Editor: Martin Leighton
Designer: Linda McVinnie
Design Assistant: Mike Snell
Sub-Editors: Wendy Gibbons, Hilary Hockman

EDITORIAL PRODUCTION
Chief: Maureen Kelly
Assistant: Deborah Fulham
Editorial Department: Theresa John, Debra Lelliott

THE CONSULTANTS: Brian Geen studied plastics technology at the Borough Polytechnic, London. He has worked in the plastics industry in both a research and a sales capacity for over 20 years.

Karl Plitt is retired from the U.S. National Bureau of Standards, where he was a physical science administrator serving as chief of the plastics and textiles sections. He has received many awards for his work in plastics technology, owns plastics patents, and is the author of numerous publications in this field.

© 1982, Time-Life Books Inc.
© 1987 Time-Life Books B.V. All rights reserved.
First European English language printing.

No part of this book may be reproduced in any form or by any electronic or mechanical means, including information storage and retrieval devices or systems, without prior written permission from the publishers, except that brief passages may be quoted for review.

ISBN 7054 0803 5

TIME-LIFE is a trademark of Time Incorporated U.S.A.

Contents

1 **Man-Made Materials: Many Uses** · 7
A Beginner's Guide to Manipulated Molecules 8
Where and How to Buy Stock 11
Preparing the Stock for Cutting or Drilling 15
Familiar Cutting Tools, Unfamiliar Techniques 20
Drilling and Counterboring 30
Rigid Sheets and Tubes Made Pliant with Heat 32
Giving Lustre and Polish to Edges and Surfaces 35

2 **A Choice of Good Connections** 41
Mechanical Devices: Joinery's Nuts and Bolts 42
Heat as a Means of Merging Thermoplastics 52
Welding Plastics with a Torch 56
Hems or Seams in Flexible Film 62

3 **A Primer on Poured Shapes** 67
Rigid Moulds to Shape Liquid Plastic Resins 68
Flexible Moulds to Hold Detail 76
Casting in a Mould: Using Resin in Liquid Form 82
Glass Fibres Reinforced with Plastic Resin 88
Tracking Down Fibreglass Flaws 94
Laminated Surfaces Move Out of the Kitchen 96

4 **A Wealth of Fillers and Paints** 101
Compounds to Patch Holes in Almost Anything 102
Watertight Fibreglass Patches 108
A New Generation of Buffered Sealants 112
Plastic-Based Coatings: Paint for Any Purpose 114
Preparing a Compatible Surface for Paint 116
The Fine Points of Application 118
Spraying the Professional Way 121

Credits and Acknowledgements 124

Index/Glossary 124

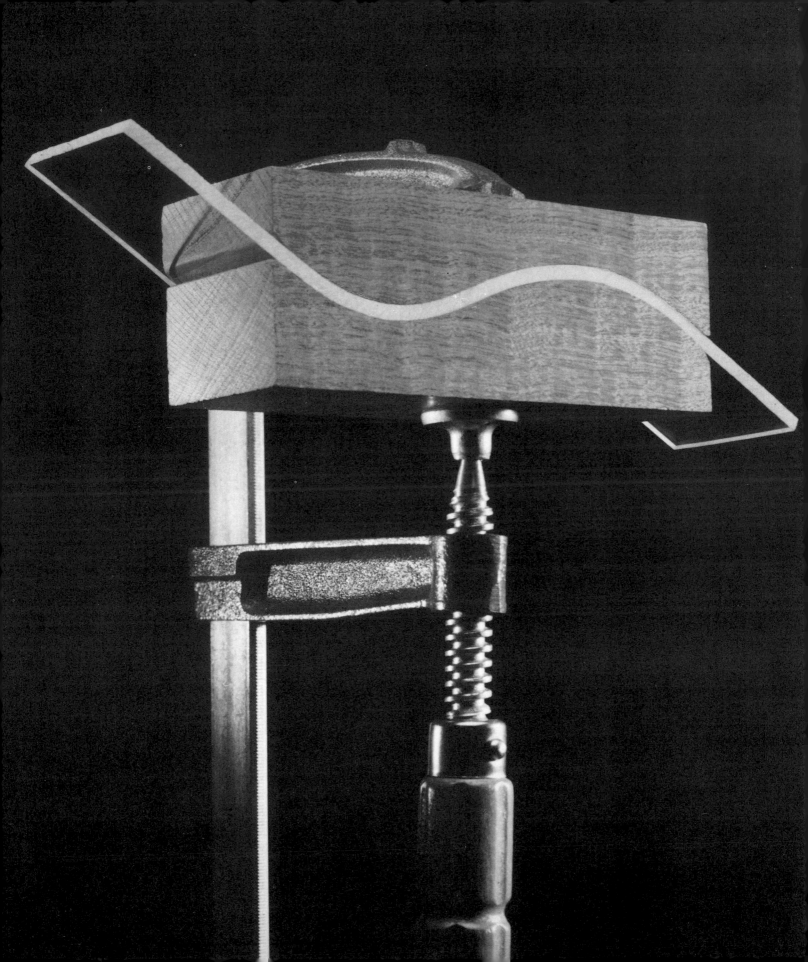

Man-Made Materials: Many Uses

Squeeze play. An oven-softened strip of sheet acrylic is moulded into an S-shape by means of a timber block sawn into two matching parts. The cramp will hold the two parts of the jig together until the plastic cools and hardens—a matter of minutes. All thermoplastics, of which acrylic is one, have this capacity to be shaped by a combination of gentle heat and pressure.

The earliest forms of plastic were developed by Alexander Parkes, an English chemist, and John Wesley Hyatt, a New York printer, who conducted independent experiments on opposite sides of the Atlantic with nitrocellulose and camphor. In 1869 Hyatt patented a material he called "celluloid", and so gave a name to the first of a family of plastics that now touch every aspect of our lives.

Once regarded as cheap substitutes for "real materials", plastics today do a vast assortment of jobs better than any natural substance can. The layers in a plywood sheet are bonded by plastic resins, the strongest of all adhesives. Gossamer-thin sheets of polyester film cover windows to form solar screens that block out 80 per cent of the sun's rays without interfering with the view. Tough, durable nylon has replaced metal in gears for many home appliances because the smooth, waxy texture of nylon gears allows them to turn quietly and efficiently without a drop of oil. Lightweight foamed plastics, sandwiched into concrete blocks and panels, often serve to insulate the foundations and walls of a house.

Amazingly, almost all of these plastics and countless others are derived from one source—petroleum. Plastics are made by breaking down the components of crude oil into simple molecules made up of hydrogen and carbon atoms, and then stringing these units into long molecular chains *(page 95)*.

The unique and widely variable forms that plastics take, as well as their lightness, strength and malleability, result in part from the variety of molecules that can be derived from petroleum and in part from the different methods chemists have devised for linking them. To further increase the range of possibilities, chemists can change characteristics of plastics with various additives. For example, the addition of microscopic whiskers of boron to epoxy resins produces a material so strong that it is used to make helicopter rotor blades.

Despite their chameleon qualities and their bewildering variety of characteristics, plastics are, on the whole, quite manageable materials. Many of the familiar tools and techniques that are employed in working with wood and metal can also be used to cut, file, shape, join and mould these synthetic substances. Indeed, plastics are so adaptable to the skills and needs of the amateur that, as sheathings, adhesives, coatings and mouldable resins, they lend themselves to literally hundreds of small and large projects designed to improve and repair the home.

A Beginner's Guide to Manipulated Molecules

Plastics, once scorned as cheap substitutes for natural materials, are now welcomed throughout the home for qualities that in many cases make them superior to the materials they replace. Rigid plastics serve as patio roofs, plumbing pipes, lighting fixtures and furniture. Flexible varieties go into garden hoses, upholstery, and food containers. As tiny particles or as liquid resins, plastics are found in many paints, sealants and adhesives. Other resins can be cast or moulded into hard, durable doorknobs and tool handles, or they can be expanded into rigid foams for insulation and insulated cups, or into supple ones for mattresses and pillows.

Despite plastics' bewildering variety, each kind—as shown in the chart on pages 12–13—offers a unique set of properties that can be used to advantage by the amateur. The most notable property of plastics is the one implied by their name: at some point during the course of their manufacture, all plastics are truly plastic—either completely liquid or pliant enough to be formed and moulded. They are organized into two distinct groups according to the circumstances under which they become plastic, or capable of being moulded.

Plastics of the first group, the thermosetting plastics, are mouldable only once, after which they solidify through a chemical process. These plastics, familiar as epoxy cements and as the hardened resins used to surface such laminates as Formica, cannot be reheated to mouldable softness; high temperatures merely char and decompose them. Those in the second group, the thermoplastics, regain their pliancy each time they are heated and can be remoulded repeatedly. They are most familiar as the vinyls used in window frames and the polyethylene of food-storage bags, as well as the hard, glossy polystyrene plastics out of which appliance casings are moulded and the clear, tough polycarbonate used for shatterproof windows.

Both kinds of plastic behaviour are a boon to the amateur. Thermosetting plastics often come as liquid resins—epoxy and polyester are commonly available—that are easy to cast at room temperature. Mixed with hardener, these plastics set to form hard and heat-resistant products ranging from a doorknob to a shower enclosure reinforced with glass fibres.

Solid thermoplastics, on the other hand, can be softened with moderate heat, then twisted, creased or bent. A seemingly rigid sheet of clear acrylic, for instance, can be softened in a kitchen oven to make fittings and furniture parts that are both decorative and practical.

Working with plastics involves many of the same shaping and finishing operations used in metalworking and woodworking. Thermoplastics parallel metals in that they can be heated for bending and can be welded. Like wood, plastics can be cut with hand and power saws, drilled, shaped with files and smoothed with sandpaper. These familiar processes, however, can sometimes take unfamiliar twists when they involve plastics. Many plastics, for example, soften at heats so moderate that the friction of a power saw, drill or sander may be enough to melt them and gum the tool. Other plastics are so flexible that they distort when sawn or drilled, making it very difficult to do accurate work. The specific remedies for these problems are presented in the pages that follow.

In many instances, the unusual charac-teristics that present problems can also be turned to advantage. Exposed to strong cleaning solutions and solvents, for example, many plastics—including most of the thermoplastics group and polystyrene in particular—weaken, crack and soften. Although this means that painstaking care must be used in matching solvent-based glues and paints to the plastic surfaces, it also makes possible a unique bonding process called solvent cementing. A bead of solvent, run along the seam, softens the adjacent plastic surfaces and the edges of the seam then bond together as the solvent evaporates.

Because they are fluid in some stage of their manufacture or use, plastics can be coloured, combined with additives or reinforcements, or expanded into foams, all of which further broadens the range of their properties and applications. Additives that can be used at home include mineral fillers that make casting resins thicker and easier to work with, as well as colouring agents. And glass-reinforced polyester is easily fabricated at home by the layering of mats of glass fibre soaked with polyester resin.

Basic Safety Rules for Working with Plastics

Working with plastics requires many of the precautions that are standard in woodworking and metalworking. There should be a first-aid kit in the work area, and power tools and heating equipment should be properly guarded. A pair of safety glasses is a must, and a dust mask is essential for operations that produce powdery residues. In addition to these basic measures, plastics call for precautions against two special dangers: irritation from fumes and inflammability.

With liquid plastics—the resins, hardeners, paints, sealants and adhesives—both hazards are immediate, and the manufacturers' toxicity labels should be read with care and acted upon. While using liquid plastics, ensure proper ventilation to disperse fumes. In many cases, you should wear a respirator with a charcoal filter *(page 67)*. Do not smoke, and never work near an open flame. Although many solid plastics are to some extent inflammable, none in common use today presents any greater fire hazard than wood. The danger from burning plastics or plastics overheated during welding or hot-bending operations is the harmful vapours that may be generated. But it is as well to keep a multipurpose, dry chemical fire extinguisher at hand when you are working with plastics, as well as to wear a respirator.

To avoid skin contact with the liquids, wear rubber gloves and a workshop apron while pouring or mixing. When sanding, drilling and sawing reinforced plastics—especially those that include glass—tiny, razor-sharp particles can be released which quickly irritate skin, eyes and lungs, so proper protective clothing is important in these situations.

The Substances of Everyday Objects

Household article	Plastic
Adhesives	
Contact cements, flexible adhesives	Silicones, synthetic rubbers
Plastic cements	Cellulosics, polystyrene
Two-component cements	Epoxies
Wood glue	PVA
Appliance housings	ABS, polystyrene, nylon, polycarbonate, PPO (Noryl)
Bath and shower enclosures	Polyester, glass-reinforced (fibreglass), acrylic
Bottles, containers	
Translucent or opaque; flexible	Polyethylene, polypropylene
Clear	Polyester, PVC, PET
Buckets, bowls	Polyethylene, polypropylene
Cushions, pillows, mattresses	Polyurethane foam, PVC foam, polyester fibres
Decorative clear castings	Acrylic, polyester
Dishes	Melamine (Melaware)
Dishwasher and washing-machine interiors	Polypropylene
Drinking glasses	
Clear and rigid	Polystyrene
Flexible	Polyethylene
Insulated cups	Polystyrene foam (Styrofoam)
Electrical circuit boards, switch toggles	Laminated epoxies and phenolics (Tufnol)
Fillers	
Caulking compounds	Polyurethane, PVA, silicones, synthetic rubbers
Grouts	PVA, silicones
Mortars	Epoxies, PVA
Putties, filler pastes	Epoxies, polyester, PVA
Patching kits	Polyester, glass-reinforced (fibreglass)
Films	
Coloured artist's films	Cellulosics
Food wrap	Polyethylene, polypropylene, PVDC (Saran)
Magnetic tape	Polyester (Mylar)
Photographic film	Cellulosics
Flooring (sheet and tiles)	PVC
Furniture	
Clear	Acrylic (Perspex, Oroglass)
Flexible	Polypropylene
Glossy and opaque	ABS, polyester, glass-reinforced (fibreglass)
Upholstered	PVC (Vynide)
Garden hoses	PVC
Gutters and downpipes	ABS, PVC
Handles and knobs	
Clear	Acrylic, cellulosics
Black, pots and pans	Reinforced phenolics

Plastics in the home. The left-hand column of the chart on the left lists the plastic household objects most likely to confront someone engaged in D.I.Y The right-hand column lists the plastics most often used for each object. In cases where a plastic is known by an abbreviation—ABS for acrylonitrile butadiene styrene, PVC for polyvinyl chloride and PVDC for polyvinylidene chloride are examples—the abbreviation is listed. Similarly, common names and widely recognized brand names are included in parentheses where helpful. In some cases, nearly identical objects are made of different kinds of plastic, depending on the manufacturer. When repairing such objects, you can tell similar plastics apart by consulting the chart on pages 12–13 and matching the plastic at hand to the one on the chart whose characteristics it most closely resembles.

continued on page 10

continued from page 9

Household article	Plastic
Insulation foams	
Preformed	Polystyrene (Styrofoam)
Foamed-in-place	Polyurethane
Lighting	
Fixtures	Reinforced phenolics
Shades, diffusers	Acrylic (Perspex, Oroglas), cellulosics, polycarbonate (Lexan, Makrolon)
Lubricants	Silicones
Paints, sealants and coatings	
Ceramic and glass	Epoxies, polyurethane
Masonry	Acrylic, epoxies, PVA, synthetic rubbers
Metal	Epoxies, phenolics
Plaster, plasterboard	Acrylic, polyester, PVA
Plastic	Polyester
Tool handles	PVC/PVA
Wood	Acrylic, polyester, PVA
Panelling and cladding	PVC
Pipes	Polyethylene, PVC
Plumbing pipes	ABS, polyethylene, PVC
Roofing	
Patio roofs	Polyester, glass-reinforced (fibreglass)
Waterproof membranes	Synthetic rubbers
Table and worktops	
Surfacing	Phenolic/melamine laminate (Formica, Warerite)
Artificial marble	Acrylic (Perspex), polyester
Telephone housings	ABS
Toys	
Glossy and opaque	ABS, polystyrene
Flexible	Polyethylene, polypropylene
Clear and hard	Polystyrene
Wallpaper	Polyester (Mylar), PVC
Window frames	PVC
Window panes, skylights clear panels	Acrylic (Perspex, Oroglas), polycarbonate (Lexan, Makrolon)

Where and How to Buy Stock

Despite the exotic names of the plastics in the chart on pages 12–13, you can buy many of them without a trip to a specialized plastics supplier. Hardware and D.I.Y. shops stock sheets of clear acrylic and polycarbonate for glazing, usually in thicknesses of 3 to 9 mm. Builders' merchants carry PVC pipe, corrugated sheets of glass-reinforced polyester used for covering patios, decorative laminates for worktops and cabinet facings, and polyethylene film. Hardware and paint shops are the best sources for many plastic-based coatings, adhesives and fillers.

Even if the particular type of plastic you need should call for a trip to a specialized plastics supplier, there are likely to be several of them listed in the classified telephone directory of any major city under the heading "Plastics – Manufacturers and Suppliers". Although a great many of these specialized plastics suppliers technically are wholesalers, you will usually not be asked to buy in wholesale quantities if you only require a small amount.

Most plastics suppliers will cut rod, sheet and tubing to size if you specify your requirements. But film or plastic sheet in a range of thicknesses is available in rolls of standard widths and lengths.

In choosing a plastic, compare your requirements with the characteristics of the plastics listed on pages 12–13. Take into account the stresses to be placed on the finished object, including the weight it will bear, its exposure to impact, abrasion and corrosive liquids, and whether it will have to endure high temperatures and direct sunlight. It is also, of course, important to consider the desired appearance of the plastic object when complete.

If the characteristics you seek do not match any plastic on the chart, the chances are that you are looking for a laminate or for a reinforced—or filled—plastic. The laminates, which are far tougher than most pure plastics, consist of layers of non-plastic materials, such as paper or cloth, bonded together with intervening layers of plastic. Filled or reinforced plastics contain materials other than plastic—most often, powdered wood or cotton fibres—that are randomly dispersed through the plastic before it sets. Such loose, fibrous fillers impart a degree of strength and resistance to chipping that is difficult to attain in any pure plastic material.

A third type of hybrid, structural foam, consists of a central core of foamed plastic sheathed in a solid, unfoamed skin of the same plastic. The structural foams offer a tough, attractive exterior and exceptional stiffness and may be made from many different sorts of plastics.

Basic plastics offspring. Layers of coarse brown paper soaked in resin form the base of a tough, moisture-proof decorative laminate *(below)*, ideal for work surfaces and cabinet facings; the penultimate layer, just beneath a surface film of clear, tough melamine, is a sheet of coloured or patterned paper. To make fibreglass, alternating layers of glass fibre mat and woven glass fibre fabric are impregnated with polyester resin. A layer of clear resin on top of the glass-reinforced layers hardens into a smooth, tough surface.

Wood or cotton fibres, scattered randomly throughout a resin, form a reinforced plastic with sufficient strength and chip-resistance to be used for coffee-pot knobs and electric-light switches. Unlike the filler in many other reinforced plastics, this filler material does not form a distinct layer in the finished plastic.

In a typical structural foam, a smooth skin of plastic covers the multicelled core. The skin is formed during manufacture when the foaming resin, injected into a closed mould under high pressure, compacts against the mould walls, yielding a light, stiff product. Structural foam is increasingly used for prefabricated housing components, such as window frames and doorframes, shutters and tiles.

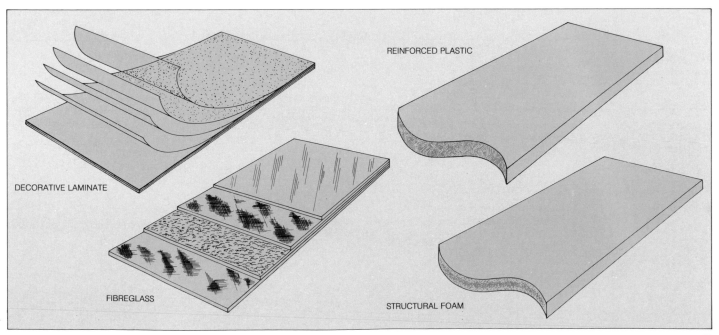

DECORATIVE LAMINATE

FIBREGLASS

REINFORCED PLASTIC

STRUCTURAL FOAM

Performance Profiles of the Major Families

Type of plastic	Characteristics	How supplied	Techniques
ABS (Acrylonitrile butadiene styrene)	Tough, hard, impact-resistant and resistant to chemicals. Usually opaque.	Rods, sheets, pipes.	Cutting, page 20 Drilling, page 30 Bending, page 32 Fastening, pages 42, 46 Finishing, page 35
Acetal	Hard and strong, resistant to chemicals, slippery, self-lubricating and brilliantly transparent. Used for valve and gear components in bathroom and kitchen appliances.	Rods, sheets.	Cutting, page 20 Drilling, page 30 Fastening, pages 52, 56
Acrylic	Prized for crystal clarity and resistance to weather. Scratches easily.	Rods, sheets, tubing; casting resins; in coatings.	Cutting, page 20 Drilling, page 30 Bending, page 32 Fastening, pages 42, 46 Finishing, page 35 Casting, page 82 Using in coatings, page 114
Cellulosics	Flexible and tough. Transparent and easily coloured. Soften at low heat.	Film, rods, sheets.	Cutting, page 20 Drilling, page 30 Fastening, pages 42, 46
Epoxies	Strong; resistant to heat and chemicals, particularly when reinforced with glass fibre. As adhesives, will bond to nearly any surface. Relatively expensive.	Resins; in adhesives, coatings, fillers.	Casting, page 82 Using in adhesives, coatings, fillers, pages 46, 102, 112, 114
Melamine	Valued for its extreme resistance to scratches, heat and chemicals. Generally laminated with paper or mixed with powdered wood or cotton fibres to reinforce it and reduce its brittleness.	Reinforced or laminated sheets.	Cutting, page 20 Drilling, page 30 Fastening, pages 46, 96
Nylon	Tough, resistant to heat and chemicals. Slippery, self-lubricating and translucent. Much used for kitchen utensils and for gears in small appliances.	Rods, sheets.	Cutting, page 20 Drilling, page 30 Fastening, pages 52, 56
Phenolics	Black or brown in colour, hard, heat-resistant. To reduce their brittleness, they are reinforced with powdered wood or cotton fibres or are laminated with paper or cloth.	Reinforced or laminated rods, sheets, or tubing; in coatings.	Cutting, page 20 Drilling, page 30 Fastening, pages 46, 96 Using in coatings, pages 114, 116
Polycarbonate	Similar to acrylic but tougher and more impact-resistant. Less clear, however, and more prone to scratching.	Rods, sheets, tubing.	Cutting, page 20 Drilling, page 30 Bending, page 32 Fastening, pages 42, 46 Finishing, page 35
Polyester	Frequently reinforced with glass fibre for strength. Easy to cast and often used for large objects. Transparent, but may yellow in sunlight.	Film; reinforced sheets; casting resins; in coatings, fillers.	Cutting, page 20 Drilling, page 30 Fastening, page 46 Casting, page 82 Reinforcing, page 88 Using in coatings, fillers, pages 102, 114 Finishing, page 35

Type of plastic	Characteristics	How supplied	Techniques
Polyethylene	Flexible, lightweight, translucent; waxy to the touch. Softens at low heat, cracks in sunlight unless pigmented black, and is permeable to odours and some gases.	Film, rods, sheets, pipes, tubing.	Cutting, page 20 Drilling, page 30 Bending, page 32 Fastening, pages 42, 52, 56, 62 Finishing, page 35
Polypropylene	Similar to polyethylene but harder and more resistant to heat.	Film, rods, sheets, tubing.	Cutting, page 20 Drilling, page 30 Bending, page 32 Fastening, pages 42, 52, 56 Finishing, page 35
Polystyrene	Hard, crystal-clear and inexpensive. Brittle; makes a distinctive clink when struck. Softens at low heat; may crack in sunlight.	Rods, sheets, foam.	Cutting, page 20 Drilling, page 30 Bending, page 32 Fastening, pages 42, 46, 62 Finishing, page 35
Polyurethane	Tough, flexible and resistant to chemicals in both its solid and its foamed forms. Often foamed in place as insulation; but like most plastics it is not fireproof and, in burning, gives off poisonous gases. Opaque.	Rods, sheets, foam, foaming compounds; in coatings, fillers.	Cutting, page 29 Fastening, page 46 Using in coatings, fillers, pages 112, 114
PVA (Polyvinyl acetate)	An important component in adhesives, paints and fillers; often chemically combined with PVC. Flexible; adheres readily to other materials.	In coatings, fillers, adhesives.	Using in coatings, adhesives, fillers, pages 46, 112, 114
PVC (Polyvinyl chloride)	Pliant, elastic, but in combination with various additives can be either flexible or rigid. Both transparent and opaque. Gives off poisonous gases at high temperature.	Film, sheets, rods, tubing, pipes; in coatings.	Cutting, page 20 Drilling, page 30 Fastening, pages 42, 46, 52, 56, 62 Using in coatings, page 114 Finishing, page 35
PVDC (Polyvinylidene chloride)	Remains strong even when extremely thin, and provides an excellent barrier against moisture and gases. Softens at low heat.	Film	
Silicones	As elastic compounds, tough and slippery to the touch. As a coating, resistant to heat and chemicals. Expensive.	Resins; in moulding compounds, coatings, lubricants, adhesives, fillers.	Using to make flexible moulds, page 76 Using in coatings, page 114 Using in fillers, adhesives, pages 46, 112
Synthetic rubbers	Tough, flexible and resistant to chemicals; important components in many coatings, adhesives and fillers. Neoprene, styrene-butadiene rubber, and nitrile rubber are among the best known.	In coatings, adhesives, moulding compounds, fillers.	Using to make flexible moulds, page 76 Using in coatings, adhesives, fillers, pages 46, 112, 114

A plastic for every purpose. The first column of this chart lists the plastics most commonly used in the home. The characteristics listed in the second column are those of the plastic unmodified with fillers or reinforcements, unless otherwise noted. "Tough" refers to resistance to scuffing and wear, "hard" to a lack of resilience and an unyielding surface, and "strong" to a resistance to tearing and crushing. The third column of the chart lists the forms in which each plastic is commonly supplied; it will enable you to see if the material with the right combination of properties comes in a shape or form that is suitable for your needs. The last column indexes specialized techniques needed for working with each of the plastics listed in the chart.

Storage System for the Raw Materials

A home warehouse in a cupboard. Store plastic sheets and long rods and tubes on end in a cupboard subdivided with chipboard into narrow compartments. Completely fill the compartments, so that the plastic is held upright, without bowing or sagging. If you cannot fill a compartment, wedge small cardboard boxes or pieces of plastic foam between the sheets or rods and the nearest divider to hold the stock vertical. Short rods and tubes may be laid flat on a shelf, but do not let them overhang the edge, lest the unsupported ends droop or sag. Wrap any unmasked rods in tissue paper to protect them against scratches, and leave the protective masking paper on plastic sheets. Never leave the cupboard open to sunlight; when masked stock is exposed to sunlight, the adhesive paper can bake on and become difficult to remove.

Liquid resins and hardeners may be stored in the same cupboard. Solvents, glues and paints should be stored elsewhere to prevent vapours from leaky containers damaging the surfaces of the sheets and rods.

The Unmasking of a Paper-Covered Sheet

Stripping off protective paper. Peel back the protective paper from one edge of the plastic sheet and hold it against a wooden dowel, such as a broom handle, about 25 to 40 mm in diameter. Holding the paper securely against the rod, roll the rod across the plastic, wrapping the paper tightly around the wood. Fasten the paper for storage and later use with a strip of masking tape. Do not uncover a greater area of plastic than you actually need to in order to bend, weld or cement the plastic.

To reuse the protective paper, release the tape securing the paper against the rod, and press the free end of the paper against the unmasked plastic. Gradually unroll the paper across the plastic, smoothing it as you go and pressing it against the plastic surface to avoid trapping air between the paper and the plastic. At the opposite edge, trim the paper with scissors, and then re-tape the unused part of the roll.

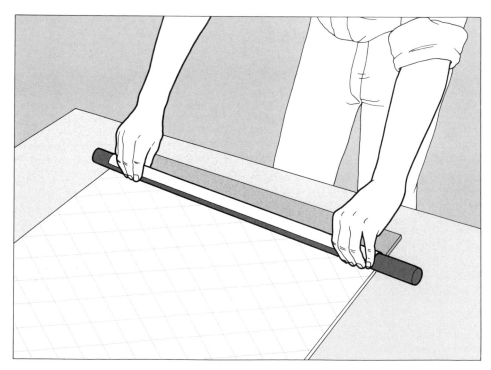

Preparing the Stock for Cutting or Drilling

Like wood and sheet metal, plastics can be sawn, drilled and sheared. Also like wood and metal, plastic stock, whether it is flat or tubular, must be clearly marked with lines for layout before the cutting tools are applied to its surface.

As they come from the factory or the supplier, plastic sheets are reliably square. So are the ends of rods and rigid tubing. However, if you are using stock that you have cut in the course of previous projects, you should check the squareness of corners, ends and edges. If necessary, true them by clamping the stock in a wooden jig and filing away any uneven plastic. Having squared the edges of the plastic, you can then calculate cuts that will minimize waste, since straight edges will not require any further trimming.

Marking the plastic surface without marring it is the crux of plastics layout: hard plastics are scratch-prone. But fortunately, the majority of plastic sheets provide a ready-made solution to the problem. At the factory, the sheets are wrapped with protective masking paper; this allows you to indicate cutting lines and locations for drill holes without touching the plastic surface. You can then cut and drill through the marked paper. If you have saved the masking-paper wrappings from previous plastics projects *(opposite page)*, you will also be able to wrap unmasked rods and tubes for marking.

Only a few tools are required for marking plastics. For straight lines on flat surfaces—sheets or the wider faces of rectangular rods—use a square and either a lead or a wax pencil, depending on whether the plastic surface is covered with masking paper. Keep in mind that any traces of wax pencil left on the plastic will bake on if the plastic is heated for bending or welding, and be sure to remove the layout lines very carefully with a damp cloth after they have served their purpose.

Remember, too, that even a carefully sharpened wax pencil leaves a line that is fairly broad, although adequate for most work. When your work calls for an especially precise cutting line, or if the plastic surface is so dark that a wax pencil will not leave a visible line, you should score the plastic lightly with a scriber. But never scribe marks other than the cutting lines: a scribed fold line or a scribed X marking a

drill hole will remain visible in the finished project and may open the way for a crack in the material. For foam plastics, both stiff and flexible, the standard marking tool is a felt-tipped or ball-point pen; test both to determine which one is best suited to the surface you are using.

When you are drawing or scribing lines on round plastic rods or tubing, a simple V-shaped jig provides both support and control. Two boards, nailed together at a right angle to form a V and propped between two rows of bricks, will serve well. So will an angle iron or a wooden beam channelled with a 90-degree V-groove. As shown on page 18, the V-shaped jig can be used to mark lines round a rod or a tube and also along its length.

Use a pair of compasses, with a pencil on one leg, to lay out arcs and circles on paper-masked plastic; use dividers, with two metal points, to scribe an unmasked surface. Before you draw a circle or an arc with a pair of compasses or dividers, build

up a foundation of several layers of masking tape at the centre of the circle to provide a firm footing for the pivot point while protecting the plastic surface.

A more complex shape can be drawn on a separate sheet of paper, then transferred in one of several ways. You can lay carbon paper between the pattern and the masked or unmasked plastic, then trace all the layout lines. Or you can cut out the pattern and fasten it directly to the sheet, rod or tube with water-soluble glue. Alternatively, you can simply scribe or draw round the cutout pattern on the plastic.

To avoid scratching unmasked plastic, cover your work surface with a soft pad of newspaper. And to reduce the chance that the completed object will crack or chip, make sure your design includes as few corners sharper than 90 degrees as possible, and no interior angles—they are common starting points for cracks. Curves and broad angles—90 degrees and up—are the safest to use with plastic sheets.

Testing a Cylinder or a Sheet for Squareness

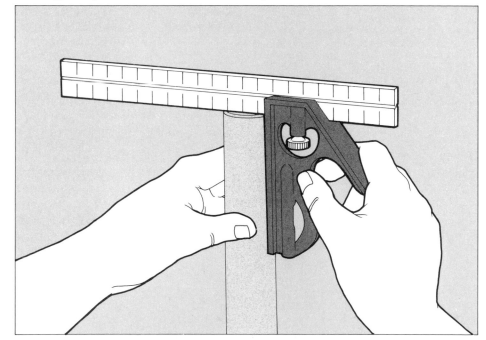

Checking rods or tubes. Fit a combination square or a try square over the end to be tested. Sight between the tool's blade and the stock: if they touch completely while the arm is held firmly against the side of the stock, the end is square. To be sure, move the tool and check the end from an angle at right angles to the first. If you find that the end is

more than 1 mm out of square, use the method shown on page 18 to scribe a true cut line round the plastic, making it as close as possible to the end of the workpiece; then saw off the uneven portion *(page 24)*. If the discrepancy is less than 1 mm, however, simply file the end of the piece until it is square *(page 16)*.

Checking a sheet for square corners. Use a steel square to check all four corners of a large sheet of plastic; use a combination square or a try square on smaller rectangles. If you find a square corner, with no space showing between the plastic's edges and the arms of the square, use the adjacent edges to determine what corrections will be needed to square the other three corners. If the sheet is more than 3 mm thick, make sure the edges are square; swing the arm of the square perpendicular to the sheet, and slide it along the edge, checking several times.

If an edge is less than 3 mm out of true, either crosswise or along its length, file it square *(opposite page, above)*. Otherwise draw or scribe a new cut line as close as possible to the uneven edge of the sheet *(opposite page, below)* and trim the plastic with a saw.

If none of the corners is square, correct the one that needs the least work, then proceed as above. To prepare an edge for filing, peel the masking paper back and lay a steel square across the plastic. Work an arm of the square towards the edge of the plastic until only the material that must be filed away to produce a square edge protrudes; then scribe a guideline to mark off the waste plastic *(below, right)*.

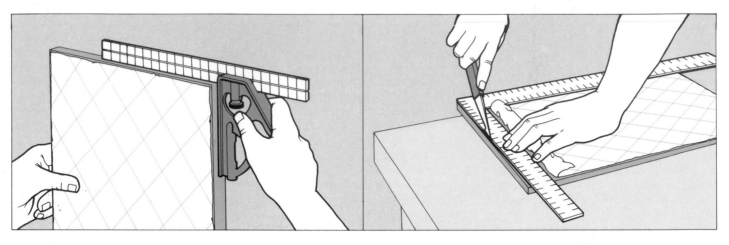

Levelling a Cylinder End

1 **Aligning the jig.** Select two boards with square ends and with widths greater than the diameter of the plastic rod or tube to be trued. Sandwich the plastic between them. With this assembly resting on a worktable, fit one end in a woodworking vice so that 50 to 75 mm extend beyond the front of the vice *(inset)*. Use a square to align the board ends, then position the rod or tube so that only the part to be filed away projects beyond the boards. Tighten the vice just enough to hold the assembly; if you are working with tubing, be careful not to crush it.

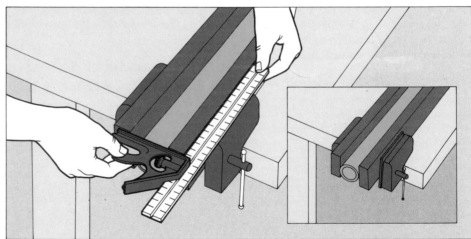

2 **Filing the end.** Use the boards as a guide while you file away excess plastic with a medium-coarse single-cut metal file until you have a perfectly square end. On soft plastics such as polyethylene, the file may clog; if it does, clean it as needed with a wire brush.

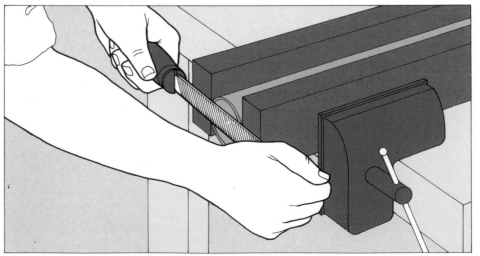

A Wooden Sandwich for Squaring Edges and Corners

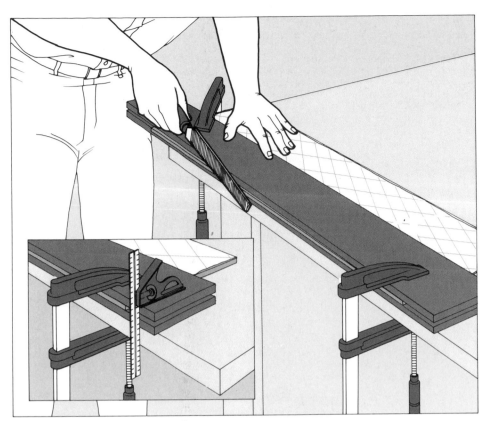

Filing away an uneven edge. Sandwich the plastic sheet between a jig made of two boards with straight edges, each a few centimetres longer than the edge to be trimmed. Align the boards with the scored guideline. To make sure that the boards are evenly placed, fit a combination square over the jig, once at each end; both boards should touch the blade *(inset)*. Secure the assembly to the edge of the workbench with two cramps; if the edge to be filed is more than 600 mm long, use three cramps. With a medium-coarse metal file, remove the excess plastic, scraping away this material with strokes running almost horizontally along the length of the plastic edge, moving the cramps as needed.

Marking Straight Cut Lines on Sheets and Cylinders

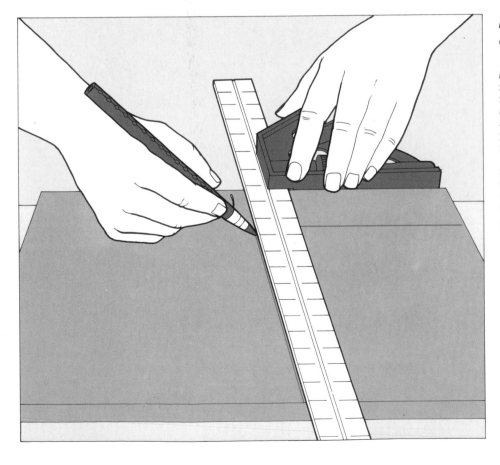

Marking sheets and square rods. Measure and mark reference points for cutting to size with a rule and, depending on the surface, a lead pencil, a wax pencil, or the point of a scriber. Then align a square or a straightedge with the reference points, and use it to guide the marking tool as you mark the cutting lines.

To indicate the position of holes to be drilled, use a pencil or a marker and the rule to mark two short intersecting lines to form an X with its centre at the centre of the planned hole. Do not scribe these lines; in most cases they would be longer than the hole's diameter and would be visible as scratches on the completed work.

Marking tubes and round rods. Lay the tube or rod in a V-shaped jig with a stop at one end; the V-groove should be no deeper than one-third the diameter of the plastic. Butt one end of the plastic against the stop, and use a ruler or a square to mark the position of the cutting line. Brace an ordinary pencil, a wax pencil, or a scriber against the edge of the jig, pressing the point firmly against the cutting-line mark; then rotate the plastic, extending the cutting-line mark completely round its circumference. Make sure that the end of the plastic stock is square to its sides and that it rests securely against the stop throughout the operation.

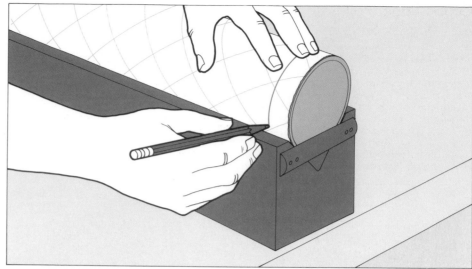

Scribing a longitudinal line. Butt the rod or tube against the stop of a V-shaped jig no deeper than one-third the diameter of the plastic. Hold the plastic securely with one hand and, using the edge of the jig as a guide, draw a line down the length of the rod or tube with a pencil, a wax pencil or a scriber.

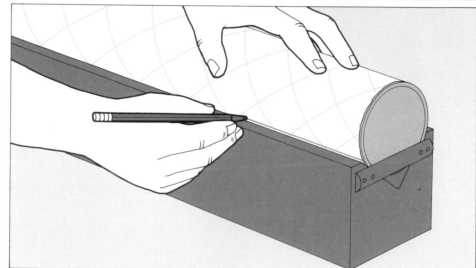

A Padded Centre Point for Swinging Curved Lines

Compasses or dividers for sheet layout. Set a pair of compasses or dividers to the radius of the curve or circle you plan. Without actually touching the plastic, use this radius to locate the centre point of the circle; for minimum waste, position the centre so that the circle or curve will touch one or more edges of the plastic sheet. Mark the centre with a pencil or a wax marker, then pad the centre with several layers of masking tape. Position the point of the compasses or the dividers against the centre, forcing the point into, but not through, the masking tape. Then draw or scribe the circle or curve.

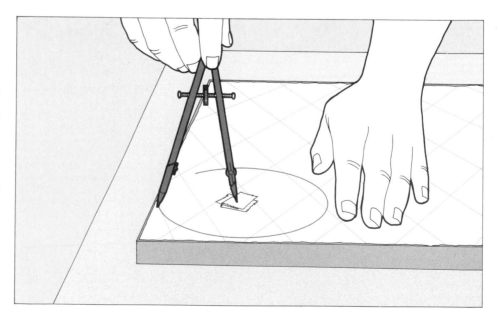

Graph-Paper Patterns
for Complex Shapes

A carbon copy for a shelf bracket. Plot the pattern for the bracket on stiff graph paper, using a steel square for the angles and straight lines and drawing the curves either freehand or with a French curve *(inset)*. Use the pattern to choose the portion of the plastic sheet to be marked and cut, and cover this area with sheets of carbon paper, inked side down. Lay the pattern over the carbon, and secure both to the plastic sheet with masking tape. Trace the pattern on to the plastic,

using a ruler for the straight portions of the pattern and drawing the curves freehand. Check to make sure all the lines have been transferred to the bare or masked plastic surface. Then remove the pattern and carbon, and cut the stock.

Make a second bracket in the same way. Glue the two brackets to the underside of a plastic shelf and to a vertical plastic support, which in turn is screwed to the wall. For instructions on gluing plastic to plastic, see pages 46–51.

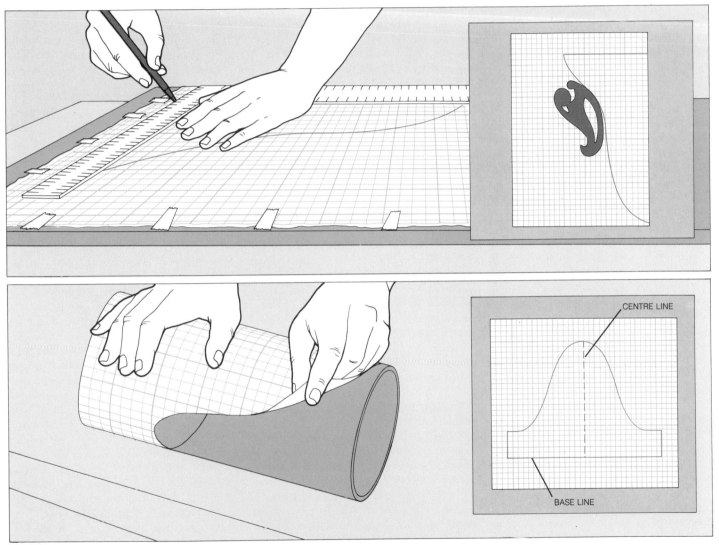

CENTRE LINE

BASE LINE

A paper pattern for a plastic scoop. Cut a pattern for the scoop from graph paper and glue it, with water-soluble glue, to a plastic tube of the desired size. In plotting the pattern, locate a base line equal to the circumference of the plastic tube, and a perpendicular centre line *(inset)*. Then construct the contours of the scoop, using a ruler for the straight sections and drawing the curved sections either freehand or with a French curve. The two sides of the scoop should be symmetrical so that their curves can be cut from the plastic tube in one operation.

In mounting the pattern on the plastic, line up the base line with the end of the tube and be sure the centre line lies along the long axis of the tube. Check to see that the edges of the pattern are well secured. When the glue is dry, cut out the scoop with a coping saw or a band saw, and file the cut edges smooth. Remove the pattern and complete the scoop by gluing a disc of plastic to the end of the tube, then shaping and gluing a handle of plastic rod to the outside face of the plastic disc. For instructions on how to glue plastics, see pages 46–51.

Familiar Cutting Tools, Unfamiliar Techniques

Almost any rigid plastic, from a worktop laminate to acrylic sheet, can be cut and shaped with the same tools used in woodworking. But the tools are not always used in quite the same way. The cutting of plastics calls for particular types of blades *(chart, page 22)* and there are some additional safety precautions. When you cut plastics with power tools, make sure the area is well ventilated, and wear eye goggles and gloves. Protection for your hands is especially important whenever you are working with rough-sawn glass-reinforced plastics or fibreglass, and a face mask is a good defence against particles when you are sawing such material.

In addition, many plastics are themselves in need of protection while they are being cut—because they are so vulnerable to scratching and chipping. Before you run a plastic sheet through any power tool, check the work surface over which the plastic will pass. Even the smallest burr or grain of sand may scratch the plastic. In fact, if the plastic is sold with a protective paper wrapping—commonly the case with acrylic—it is best to leave the paper in place while the plastic is being machined.

If the plastic has no protective wrapping, you can cover it with brown paper or cardboard, held in place with masking tape or water-soluble glue. In place of a wrapping, you can cover the work surface with paper, cardboard or a piece of felt. When clamping a scratch-prone plastic, always place a wooden block between the plastic and the jaws of the cramp—whether or not the plastic has a protective wrapping.

During cutting, most sheet plastic will need support to keep it steady. It should rest on a fairly large work surface and be pressed down firmly to reduce vibration. The cut should fall slightly to the waste side of the cutting line, to allow for edge finishing *(page 35)*.

Almost any saw, even a carpenter's fine-toothed crosscut, can cut most plastics, but power saws are the most effective because the right blade for cutting the material can be chosen and worn blades can be replaced easily. For straight edges on plastic sheets over 2 mm thick, a circular saw is pre-ferred because it produces the smoothest cut. Overheating can be avoided if you use Teflon-coated blades and blades with buttress-type teeth that are wider than the thickness of the blade and so reduce friction. The rate of feeding a plastic sheet into a circular saw can only be judged by experience of working with different materials and thicknesses.

Jigsaws cut all types of plastics and also handle a range of cuts, such as bevels and curves. They are especially good for cutting intricate patterns or small-radius circles in plastics up to 12 mm thick. However, it is important to fit them with fine-toothed blades when you are cutting fibreglass or glass-reinforced plastics.

When cutting with a jigsaw, stop the saw and back it out as soon as it starts to bind. Unfortunately, the heat of a power tool's fast-moving blade tends to melt the plastic and clog the teeth of the saw. It may even fuse together the cut plastic edges behind the blade, trapping the blade in the work.

In general, the problem of "melt-down" is easier to deal with when you use larger power tools such as circular saws and band saws. Often the speed of these saws can be adjusted downwards and a lubricant—beeswax, oil, soap or water—may be added to lower the temperature. Two additional advantages of a band saw are that the plastic chips are dislodged from its blade as it travels round its circuit, and that the blade has a chance to cool before it re-enters the cut. However, the wheels over which the blade travels will occasionally need to be cleaned with a wire brush.

Unfortunately, plastics quickly dull saw blades. For this reason, it may be wise to keep an assortment of blades exclusively for working with plastics. Any blade made for cutting plywood is suitable, if it has the necessary number of teeth per 25 mm, but there are also blades made especially for cutting plastics and so labelled. The blades that will stay sharpest are carbide-tipped ones—available for band, circular and table saws—but they are also more expensive than ordinary blades.

In cutting laminates, especially those not backed with plywood, a major problem is likely to be chipping and cracking, but there are several ways to minimize the risk. One is to press transparent tape over the cutting line. Another is to round the interior corners of openings in worktops, such as those for a set-in sink; both during and after cutting the laminate, rounded corners are less likely to split than square ones. A third way to protect the laminate from damage, useful when working with a handsaw, is to place the decorative surface face up and hold the saw at a low angle, moving it along in short strokes.

For trimming away excess laminate and shaping a corner at the same time *(page 98)*, a router is useful. It can also cut a V-groove in acrylic so that the piece, when heated, can be bent to a right angle, forming a sharp interior corner *(page 32)*. As with power saws, if you often use a router for plastics, it pays to invest in a special carbide-tipped router bit.

Some plastics can be cut without a saw. For example, acrylic up to 6 mm thick can be scored and snapped in two—but only when the piece removed is at least 40 mm wide and only when the acrylic is unpatterned, because the bumps in the pattern will cause an uneven score and break. For this technique, shown opposite, you will need a steel square and a 19 mm dowel, as well as a nail, a linoleum cutter or a special scoring tool designed for plastics. The plastic is snapped while the protective masking paper is still in place, and the paper is cut with a knife or a razor blade.

Small rods and tubing that have low-impact strength and are rigid, made of materials such as acrylic and polycarbonate, can also be cut without a saw. First a notch is filed at the cutting line, then the piece is snapped apart, with the notch facing away from the body and the thumbs of both hands together and behind the notch. Less rigid materials, such as PVC, nylon and ABS, are best cut with a hacksaw supported in a V-block *(page 18)*.

Thin plastics, such as acetate and very thin laminate, can be cut with paper cutters, tin snips, or large scissors specially designed for the purpose. Such tools are available in D.I.Y. shops.

Scoring and Snapping
a Sheet of Acrylic

1 Preparing the acrylic for scoring. Mark the break line on the protective paper covering the acrylic sheet, and lay a steel square along the line, clamping both sheet and square to a workbench. Position the break line as far in from the edge of the workbench as the jaws of the cramps will allow. Be sure the positions of the cramps leave the break line free.

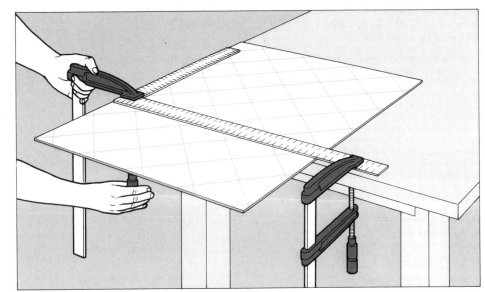

2 Scoring the acrylic. Using the steel square as a guide, score the acrylic repeatedly along the break line with a trimming knife or a scoring tool. Apply firm, even pressure along the full length of the line, allowing each stroke to run off the edge of the plastic, on to the workbench. The tool should produce a thin, continuous curl on each pass. Make about 25 passes for sheets that are up to 5 mm thick, and about 35 passes for sheets up to 7 mm thick.

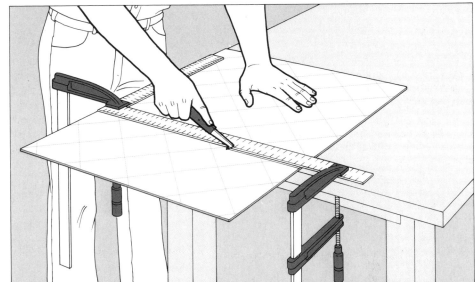

3 Breaking the sheet. Release the sheet and move it to the centre of the workbench, positioning the scored line, face up, over a 19 mm dowel that is at least as long as the line. Brace the wide part of the sheet with one hand and press down on the narrow part, using the dowel as a fulcrum. The sheet should snap cleanly in two.

If the sheet does not break in a single movement, place your hands at the edge closest to you and apply pressure until a break begins. Then move your hands along the line, keeping the heels of your hands about 50 mm ahead of the point where the break ends, gradually elongating the break until the sheet snaps in two. Cut the protective paper with a razor blade or a knife.

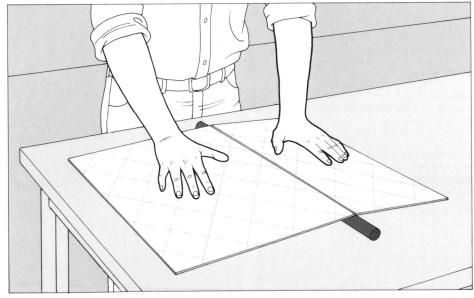

Using Body Leverage to Break a Large, Thin Sheet

Snapping up against a straightedge. Mark the break line on both sides of the sheet of laminate or acrylic, aligning them exactly, and score one side the necessary number of times, as in Step 2, page 21. Place the sheet on the floor, scored side down, wedging two pencils under the outer edge of the section to be snapped. Lay a board on the other section, wide enough to stand on and at least as long as the width of the sheet. Align the edge of the board with the break line, and secure the board to the sheet with heavy tape. Then stand on the board and pull up on the free section, snapping the sheet in two.

If the sheet is very wide, get a helper to stand on the board while you stand off the sheet and raise it up to break it. Cut through the protective paper over the break with a trimming knife.

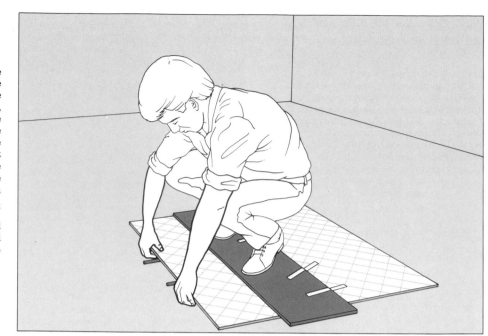

Blade Types for Large Power Tools

Choosing the best blade for the job. The chart on the right indicates the best choice of saw blades to use with large power tools for cutting plastics of varying kinds and thicknesses. Listed vertically in two general categories—band saw and circular saw or table saw—are the materials to be cut, the type of blade and the number of blade teeth per 25 mm. In each case the blade listed is the optimum choice, but substitutions are possible. For example, on the band saw, all the listed types and thicknesses of plastics can be satisfactorily cut with a skip-tooth wood-cutting blade. And although a carbide-tipped circular saw blade is ideal for those plastics with which it is paired, a hollow-ground blade for cutting plywood also does the job. The blades listed have odd names but are commonly available. Skip-tooth blades have a tooth-wide gap between teeth; ordinary blades for wood or metal have no gap between the teeth. Hollow-ground blades are made with teeth wider than the blade plate, and spring-set blades have teeth that point in alternating directions.

On a variable-speed band saw, adjust the speed to the material. Cut laminates, polystyrene foam and thin plastic such as 6 mm acrylic at top speed: on home models this is usually 1,000 metres per minute. Tough plastics, such as phenolics and polycarbonate, should be cut at low speed, about 500 metres per minute. PVC, cellulosics and thick acrylic should be cut at middle speed, about 750 metres per minute.

	Material to be cut	Type of blade	Teeth per 25 mm
Band saw	1.5–6 mm acrylic	Regular metal-cutting	5–7
	6–23 mm acrylic	Regular metal-cutting or skip-tooth	5–7
	25 mm and over acrylic	Skip-tooth	5–7
	Laminates	Regular metal-cutting	3–8
	Up to 75 mm cellulosics	Skip-tooth	4–6
	Phenolics, melamine	Regular metal-cutting	6–10
	Epoxies, polyester, acetal, polycarbonate	Regular metal-cutting	10–18
	Polystyrene foam	Regular metal-cutting	10–18
	Polyurethane foam (rigid)	Skip-tooth	4–6
	Polyvinyl chloride (PVC)	Regular metal-cutting or skip-tooth	6–9
Circular saw or table saw	1.5–6 mm acrylic	Carbide-tipped	8–14
	6–19 mm acrylic	Carbide-tipped	5–8
	19 mm and over acrylic	Carbide-tipped or spring-set	3–4
	Epoxies, melamine, phenolics, polyester	Carbide-tipped	8–10
	PVC, polystyrene foam, acetal, cellulosics, polycarbonate	Hollow-ground plywood-cutting	4–6
	Laminate	Carbide-tipped	6–10
	Polyurethane foam (rigid)	Hollow-ground plywood-cutting	4–6

Accurate Band-Saw Cutting with the Aid of Fences

1 Setting up the saw. Install the proper blade *(chart, opposite page)* and set the saw for the correct speed; then set the blade guides 3 mm higher than the acrylic sheet. Measure the distance from the cutting line, marked on the sheet, to the waste edge of the sheet, then set the saw's rip fence this distance from the blade. Check the distance from the fence to the edge of the saw table at several points, to be sure the fence is parallel to the table edge and consequently to the plane of the saw blade.

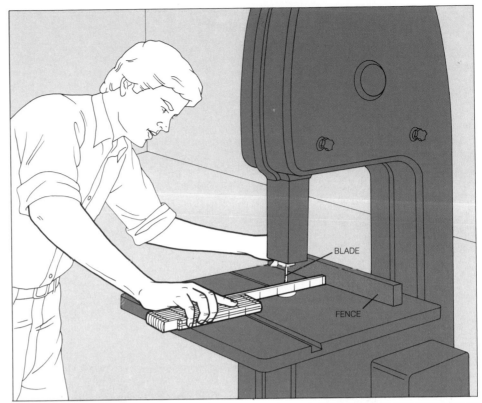

BLADE

FENCE

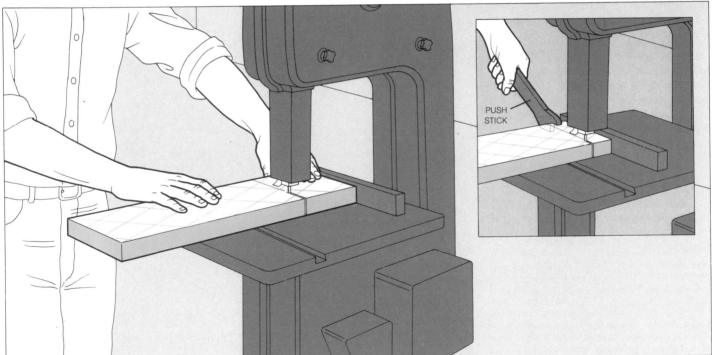

PUSH
STICK

2 Making the cut. With the saw turned on, butt the acrylic sheet against the fence and push the sheet forwards against the blade. The blade should enter the sheet just to the waste side of the cutting line. Feed the plastic carefully and steadily past the blade, until the cut is complete. If one part of the stock you are working with is less than 75 mm wide, you should use a push stick to help move the stock past the blade *(inset)*, thus avoiding any risk of injury to your hands.

Forming a Bevelled Edge with Power Saws

Using a table saw. Select the appropriate blade for the plastic *(page 22)* and set it at the desired angle, with the blade just higher than the thickness of the plastic. Clamp a piece of timber to the table-saw fence so it extends from the near edge of the table to just short of the midpoint of the blade. Align the cutting line of the plastic with the saw blade, then adjust the timber and the saw fence to act as a guide for the right-hand edge of the plastic.

Once the cutting position has been established, pull back the plastic and turn on the saw. Then push the plastic past the blade, using the mitre gauge as a pusher.

Bevelling with a jigsaw. Set the saw base plate at the desired angle, and clamp the plastic to a workbench, sandwiching it between the table and a piece of 12 mm plywood. Position the plastic so that the cutting line overhangs the bench edge; place the plywood over it so that the distance from the plywood edge to the cutting line equals the distance from the saw blade to the edge of the base plate. Then turn on the saw and begin the cut, pressing the side of the base plate firmly against the plywood.

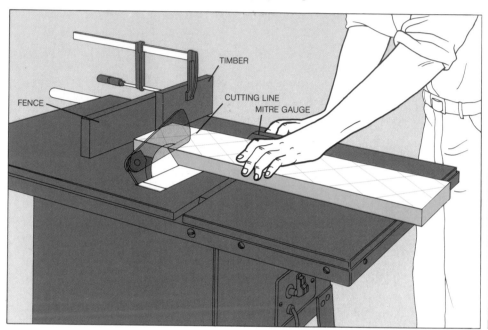

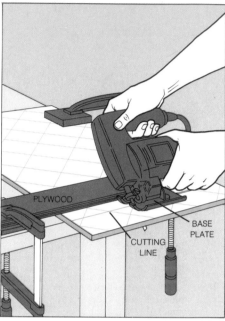

Sawing Tubes and Rods

Using a table saw with round stock. Hold the plastic tube, here PVC pipe, against the face of the mitre gauge. To position the stock, hold the plastic against the saw blade, aligning the blade with the cutting line. To cut tubing, turn on the saw, hold the tubing against the mitre gauge and feed the tubing into the saw blade until the tubing is over the centre of the blade. Then begin to revolve the tubing, rolling it towards you, meanwhile holding it securely against the mitre gauge. Continue revolving the tubing until you have cut completely round its circumference. File off any rough edges.

To cut a solid circular rod, raise the saw blade until it is about 2 mm higher than the diameter of the rod. Brace the rod against the mitre gauge, and push the rod through the saw blade. For a rod that is greater than 75 mm in diameter, mark the stock, push it past the blade, then turn it over and cut the other side.

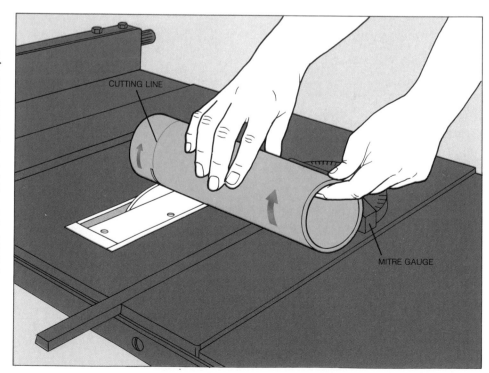

Running round stock through a band saw. Set the blade guides of the saw so that they are 3 mm higher than the diameter of the tubing or rod. To prevent the plastic from spinning when it passes through the saw blade, hold it firmly against the mitre gauge. Then slowly feed the plastic, here PVC pipe, into the blade until it is cut in two. For rods and tubing of small diameter, you can use a block of wood cut with a V-groove to hold the work steady *(inset)*.

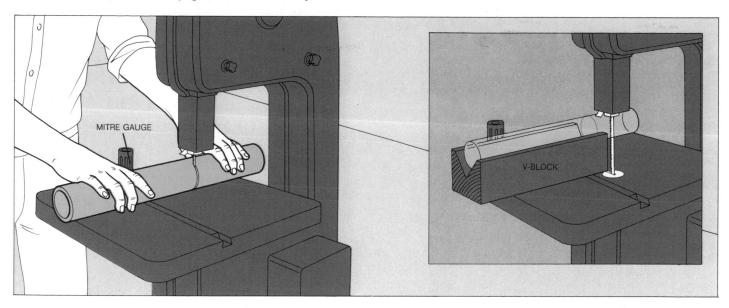

Curve-Cutting Techniques

Contouring with a band saw. Prepare the saw by fitting it with the correct blade *(page 22)*, setting it for the proper speed, and adjusting the blade guides to sit 3 mm higher than the thickness of the plastic. Turn on the saw and guide the plastic forwards until the blade touches the waste side of the cutting line. Feed the piece steadily against the blade, pushing as fast as the blade will cut easily and stopping only if the blade overheats and sticks. If overheating recurs, moisten the blade with soap, oil or Teflon spray.

For an intricate contour, begin with a rough cut, then gradually come closer to the cutting line in several repeated cuts. Use the finishing techniques shown on page 36 to take the piece of plastic down to its final shape.

Shaping curves with a jigsaw. Clamp the plastic to a worktable so that part of the cutting line overhangs the table edge *(below, left)*. Turn on the saw and cut into the plastic from a waste edge, coming into the cutting line at a shallow angle. Follow the cutting line as far as you can, until the table edge gets in the way. Then turn off the saw, ease it out of the cut and reclamp the plastic so that another section of cutting line overhangs the table edge. Reinsert the blade just behind where you left off, switch on the saw and continue to cut. Repeat this procedure until the entire curve is complete.

To cut curves in thin plastic with a jigsaw, first sandwich the plastic between two slightly larger pieces of 6 mm plywood, nailing through the edges of the plywood to fasten the sandwich together *(below, right)*. As you nail through the plywood, be careful that you are not nailing into the plastic. Draw the cutting line on the plywood and then clamp the sandwich to the worktable, proceeding as described above. You can use a coarse blade for this job, if you wish, since it has to be able to cut through the plywood.

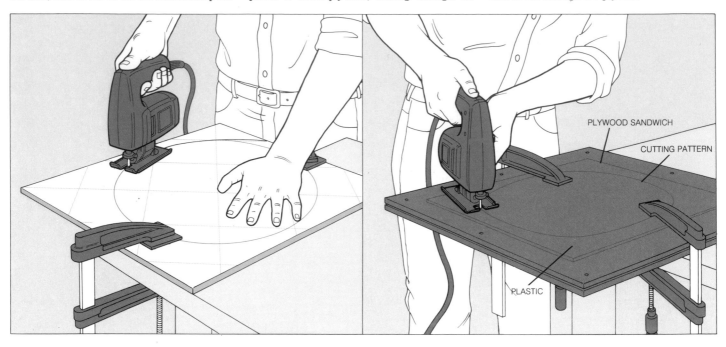

Routing a V-Groove for a Square Inside Corner

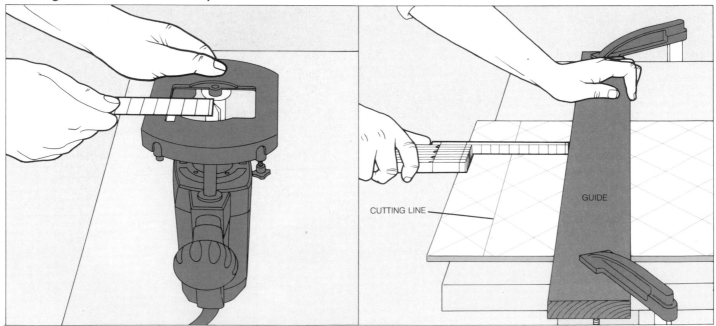

1 **Setting up the cut.** Draw a cutting line on the protective paper covering the plastic, marking the centre of the planned groove, and fit a V-groove bit into the router. Set the tip of the bit flush with the router base and measure the distance from the bit tip to the straight edge of the base *(above, left)*. Then set a straight-edged guide on the plastic, placing the guide this distance from the cutting line *(above, right)*. Clamp the guide in place and recheck your measurements.

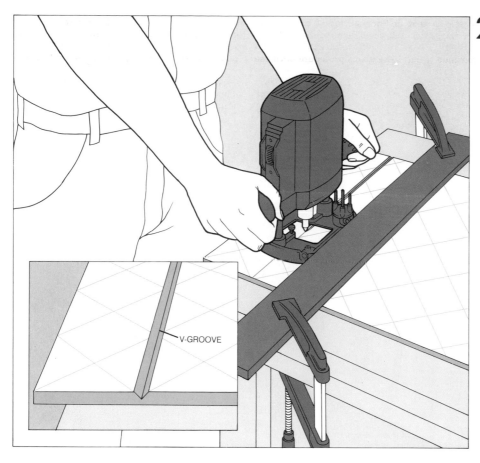

2 **Routing the groove.** Set the depth of the router bit at half the thickness of the plastic. Place the router at one end of the cutting line with the straight side of its base pressed against the guide and its bit just clear of the edge of the plastic. Turn on the router and draw it along the guide to make a V-shaped groove *(inset)*.

V-GROOVE

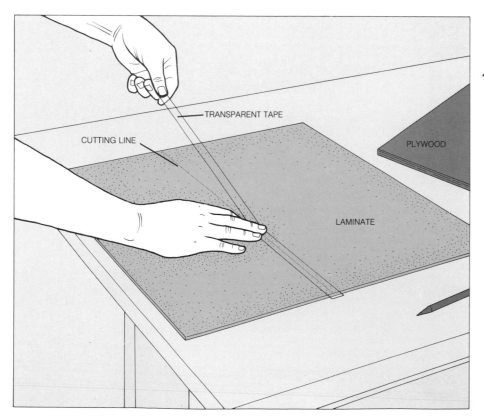

A Professional's Way to Cut Through Laminate

1 **Preparing the cutting surface.** Place the laminate, decorative side up, on a worktable; mark the cutting line, then cover the line with a length of transparent tape. Place the laminate so that the cutting line overhangs the edge of the table by 25 to 50 mm. Clamp a piece of plywood over the laminate, positioning the plywood so that its edge can be used as a cutting guide; the plywood will also help to control the vibration of the laminate as a circular saw cuts through it.

TRANSPARENT TAPE

CUTTING LINE

PLYWOOD

LAMINATE

2 **Sawing the laminate.** Fit the circular saw with a plywood-cutting blade that has six to 10 teeth per 25 mm, and set the blade depth to 50 mm. Place the saw at one end of the cutting line; then turn on the saw and push it forwards, using the edge of the plywood as a guide.

To cut a large piece of laminate in two, set up the work as in Step 1, with the cutting line overlapping the edge of the table by a few centimetres; but with a larger piece you must rest the unsupported end of the laminate on sawhorses or a table of similar height.

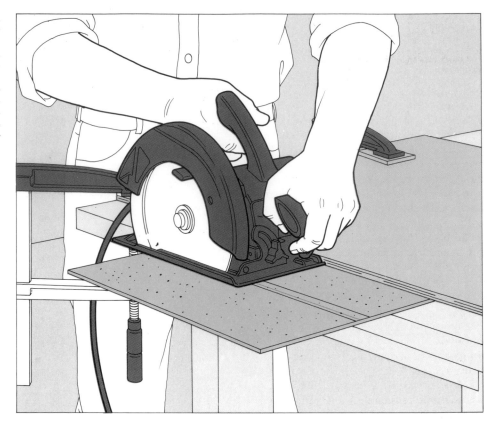

Making an Interior Cut in a Sheet of Laminate

Setting up the work. After marking the cutting line, clamp the laminate, decorative side up, to a piece of scrap plywood, hardboard or chipboard and place the work on two lengths of 100 by 50 mm timber laid across sawhorses. Drill a pilot hole for the saw blade near the inside of the cutting line. Insert the saw blade in the hole and cut round the outline.

If the laminate is already glued to a plywood base, as for a sink in a countertop, eliminate the lengths of timber and the ply or chipboard, and rest the work directly on the sawhorses.

When cutting a glass-reinforced plastic or material that is stiff enough not to need backing but also brittle—a synthetic marble, for instance—never attempt to cut square corners; they create stress points that may cause the laminate to crack. To round corners with a tight radius, drill a hole at least 25 mm in diameter at each corner with a hole saw *(page 30)* or a drill, then connect the holes to complete the outlines.

PILOT HOLE

OUTLINE

Cutting Rigid or Flexible Foams

Plastic foams can be either rigid or flexible, and they require different cutting methods. Rigid foams such as polystyrene and polyurethane can be cut with most of the same tools and techniques used for acrylic *(pages 20–26)*. A jigsaw or band saw, for example, will make quick work of cutting curved or straight lines in rigid foam. In this case the band saw should be fitted with a wood-cutting or metal-cutting skip-tooth blade having less than 10 teeth per 25 mm *(chart, page 22)*.

A table saw will also cut rigid foam quickly, but it is limited by its blade height to foams less than 75 mm thick. Thin sheets of rigid foam, up to 12 mm thick, can be cut with a scalpel, and very thin sheets can be cut with a guillotine or with tin snips. Commercially, rigid foams such as expanded polystyrene are often cut with a hot wire cutter, a resistance wire attached under tension to two terminals and controlled by a variable resistor.

Flexible foams require more ingenuity because they cannot be cut with the power tools associated with woodworking. For thin flexible foam, a razor blade or scissors are usually satisfactory, and an electric carving knife is an excellent tool for cutting straight lines or contours in thicker types of flexible foam.

Rough or uneven edges on rigid foam can be smoothed with a forming tool. Uneven edges on flexible foam are more difficult to deal with, so it is best to make the initial cut as carefully as possible. However, most flexible-foam edges will eventually be concealed by the upholstery fabric that usually covers them.

Using an Electric Carving Knife to Shape Foam

Making a straight cut. Set the foam on a worktable, positioning it so the cutting line overhangs the table edge by at least 25 mm. To begin the cut, hold the electric knife at a 45-degree angle to the top plane of the foam, and draw it into the foam about 50 mm. Then move the knife to a perpendicular position and continue cutting. Be sure to keep your fingers clear of the blade.

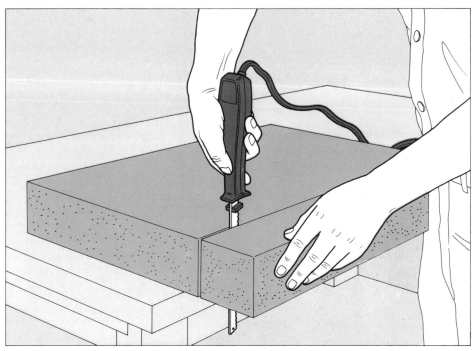

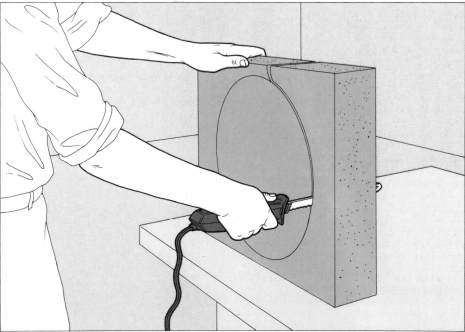

Cutting curved shapes. Stand the foam on edge, cutting outline facing you, and start the cut at the top edge. Follow the outline, keeping the knife blade perpendicular to the foam surface. To make cutting less awkward, stop the knife from time to time and change the position of the foam so you are always cutting downwards.

For an interior cut, puncture the foam with a sharp knife, and push the electric-knife blade through the slit. Proceed as above.

Drilling and Counterboring

Drilling holes in plastics, for fasteners or for decoration, is done with many of the same tools that are used for drilling holes in metal and wood. But added procedures and precautions are needed, to accommodate plastics' incompressibility, brittleness and low softening temperatures.

The first of these, incompressibility, calls for greater accuracy in drilling holes that must align: wood fibres will compress to a certain extent when a bolt, screw or plug penetrates two holes that do not precisely match, but some plastics will crack in this situation. Where alignment of two holes is important, therefore, it is best to use a drill press or to mount a portable drill in a drill stand.

In less critical situations, holes can be drilled freehand with a manual drill or a power drill. When you are using a variable-speed power drill, the speed setting should be in the slow range (500 to 1,000 rpm) with a high-speed twist bit, and in the high range (up to 5,000 rpm) with a Forstner bit. The drill should always be fed into the work slowly and steadily but without excessive pressure, then slowed even more as the tip nears the break-through point on the opposite side.

For the actual piercing of the plastic, a high-speed twist bit is preferable, particularly when you need to penetrate all the way through stock. But the bit needs modification to stop it from splitting or cracking the plastic as it cuts.

The tip of the bit must be blunted very slightly to stop it from causing small split lines on the other side of the plastic. Except on very thin plastics, the blunted tip permits the full width of the bit to enter the stock before the tip breaks through on the opposite side, stabilizing the drill's action so that it cuts a straight, clean hole. The two sharp leading edges of the bit, called the cutting lips, should also be blunted, so that they plough rather than slice their way along. Some twist bits made for plastics include these blunted features, but it is an easy enough matter to convert an ordinary twist bit with a file.

The configuration of the bit will depend on the size and type of hole needed. A brad-point bit, a Forstner bit or the drill fitting called a hole saw will work well for drilling plastics. And for countersinking fasteners, you can use the counterbore, countersink and combination drill-countersink bits designed for working with wood.

As further precautions against chipping the plastic, leave the protective paper in place until the drilling is complete. In anchoring the plastic to a work surface or in a vice, use scrap timber to protect the plastic surface from the jaws of the cramp or vice. Working with the plastic at room temperature, rather than when the material is cold, will also discourage chipping.

The low softening temperature of some plastics is both a bane and a blessing in drilling. Bits cutting deep holes should be backed out often to clear swarf away. Bits should not be stopped in the hole, lest they be seized by plastic cooling round them. On the other hand, the softened plastic lends itself to a technique for producing a clean, smooth hole. Drill a pilot hole slightly smaller than the ultimate hole, and put oil or wax into it. Then drill again with the correct sized bit—the lubricant helps to expel any swarf and combines with the softened plastic to leave the walls of the hole smooth and shiny.

Drill bits for plastics work. A high-speed twist bit, with its tip slightly blunted, is the best choice for drilling plastics. One designed for wood-cutting will drill holes in acrylic; a metal-cutting type is best for tough thermoplastics such as nylon, polycarbonate and cellulosics. A brad-point bit, available in diameters of up to 25 mm, is good if you are drilling holes that go just part way through the plastic.

A Forstner bit can be used to counterbore holes, and a hole saw, available in diameters of up to 112 mm, is useful for large holes in any thickness of plastic. A pilot bit in the centre of the hole saw positions the saw on the work, and knockout holes in the sides make it easy to push out the cut disc.

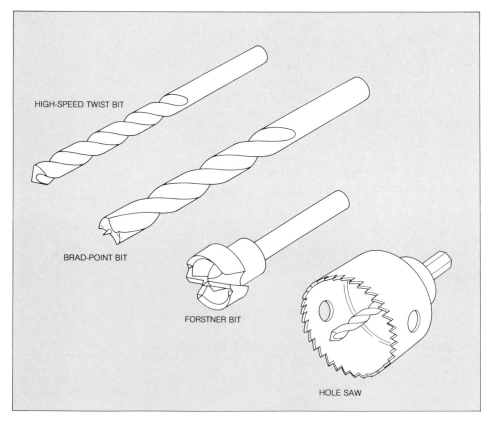

HIGH-SPEED TWIST BIT

BRAD-POINT BIT

FORSTNER BIT

HOLE SAW

Modified Wood Bits, Special Supports

1 Modifying the bit. Round the tip of the bit with a metal file or a bench grinder. Then file or grind the two sharp edges of the cutting lips, making both uniformly blunt. The drawing below shows a twist bit before *(left)* and after *(right)* modification. The cutting angle has been changed so that the drill will emerge without fracturing the plastic. Check the bit by drilling a hole in a scrap of acrylic. The drill should produce continuous spirals of waste plastic of equal width. Before drilling, use a punch to make a small dent to hold the tip in place.

2 Drilling the hole. Clamp the plastic in a vice between two pieces of scrap timber; the scrap behind the work should be large enough to back up the hole. Turn on the drill and apply even pressure to bore the hole.

On a drill press, back the plastic where the hole is to be drilled with a piece of timber. Centre the hole mark under the bit; clamp the timber and plastic to the table, using additional pieces of scrap timber to protect the plastic from the cramp jaws. Drill as above.

For large holes in thin plastic, place scrap wood over as well as under the plastic, and drill through the sandwich. For holes in round stock, use a V-block *(page 18)* to hold the rod or tubing, and clamp the V-block to the work surface.

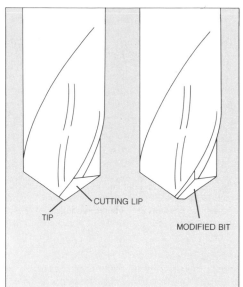

CUTTING LIP

TIP

MODIFIED BIT

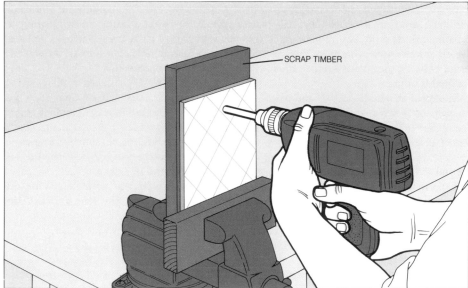

SCRAP TIMBER

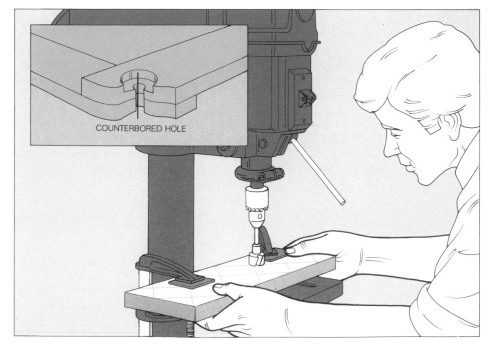

COUNTERBORED HOLE

A Two-Part Hole

Counterboring a hole for a bolt head. Fit a Forstner bit or a hole saw into the drill press and centre the hole mark under the tip of the bit. Clamp the plastic to the drill-press table, protecting the plastic from the cramp jaws with timber scraps. No backing is needed when the hole is being drilled only part way through the plastic. Set the depth stop on the drill press, turn on the drill and lower the bit to make the first cut. Then replace the Forstner bit with a twist bit 2 mm larger than the diameter of the bolt. Check to ensure the tip of the twist bit lines up with the small hole left by the tip of the Forstner bit. Put a piece of wood behind the plastic. Reset the depth stop, then drill the second hole.

To drill a matching bolt hole in the second piece of plastic, align the pieces, and push a pencil or an awl through the top piece to mark the second one. Set the depth stop and, using the same twist bit, drill the matching hole *(inset)*.

Rigid Sheets and Tubes Made Pliant with Heat

Several plastics have the useful property of becoming pliable when they are heated to temperatures ranging from 120 to 150°C. Once heated, they can be bent into a variety of new shapes.

The plastics best suited for heating and bending at home are acrylic (commonly sold as perspex) and polyvinyl chloride (PVC) pipe. The acrylic, fabricated in sheets of various thicknesses that may be transparent, translucent, tinted, or even mirrored, is often used for making room dividers, break-resistant windscreens and windows. PVC pipe, available in many different colours and diameters, is most commonly seen in plumbing waste systems and drainage installations.

Sheets of acrylic that are 3 mm thick become pliable when exposed to 150°C heat for about four minutes; sheets that are 6 mm thick—the thickest that it is practical to bend at home—need to be exposed to 150°C for about 10 minutes. PVC pipe softens much faster: in about a minute at the lower temperature of 120°C. Neither plastic should be exposed to heat over 150°C: both of them may bubble, scorch and undergo irreversible molecular and structural change if overheated.

Acrylic and PVC pipe cool rapidly and should be shaped quickly while they are at their maximum forming temperature. In most cases acrylic should be bent about 5 degrees beyond the desired finished angle, then allowed to retract to that angle, at which point it should be held or clamped for a few minutes of final cooling; PVC pipe should be overbent by as much as 20 degrees. Overbending is necessary because the polymers in the plastic *(page 95)* will tend to resist the bend and to return to their former configuration as they cool—a phenomenon known as "memory". When the acrylic is completely cool, this tendency is thwarted, and the polymers are in effect frozen in place. The memory phenomenon has one useful result: it permits novices to correct mistakes and try again simply by rewarming the plastic.

For bending localized areas of plastic, use a hot-air gun of the type commonly used for stripping paint. These have temperature controls and can be fitted with a variety of nozzles to diffuse the heat. To shape acrylic sheets, hot air is directed over the bend line until the plastic softens; the sheet can then either be bent by hand and the final configuration judged by eye *(opposite page, centre)* or, for greater precision, it can be bent over a plywood form *(opposite page, bottom)*.

Before applying a hot-air gun to PVC pipe, the pipe must be filled with dry sand to stop its walls from collapsing as it is bent *(page 34)*. PVC pipe that has been heated and bent more than once is weakened by the process, and should not be used for plumbing.

When a bend line is warmed by a hot-air gun, the final form can be no more than two sides of an angle. If you need to heat a complete sheet of acrylic in order to shape the plastic into more complex forms, you can use a domestic oven—but to minimize the risk of releasing toxic fumes you must take strict precautions. Preheat the oven to the required temperature, then turn off the gas or electricity before putting the acrylic sheet into the oven on a clean baking tray. Ensure that the room is well ventilated, and leave the oven door slightly ajar while the plastic is heating. Once the sheet is pliable, you can use a variety of forming agents—a cylindrical food container, perhaps, or the matching halves of a wooden mould cut on a jigsaw, or blocks and cramps that will hold the plastic in a more complicated multiangled shape until it is cool *(page 34, above)*.

Because acrylic, styrenic and PVC materials can emit poisonous or corrosive fumes when overheated, good ventilation and no smoking are vital when using either a hot-air gun or an oven. Never allow plastic to come into direct contact with a naked flame, and do not leave the plastic unattended while it is being heated.

Although acrylic can be bent into an acute angle, the actual apex of the angle will be slightly rounded—unless you adopt a special procedure. A sharp interior corner can be achieved if a V-groove is cut along the bend line before the acrylic is heated; the groove should be half as deep as the thickness of the plastic sheet *(page 27)*. When the plastic is bent, the V will form a sharp inside corner; the outside of the corner, however, will be rounded.

Despite the ease with which acrylic and PVC pipe can be bent, there are pitfalls. One, to which acrylic is vulnerable, is scratching. To protect the acrylic surface, it is best to leave its masking paper in place except in areas that are to be heated. All paper must be removed, of course, from plastic that will be heated in an oven. But when you use a hot-air gun to soften the plastic, all of the paper can be left in place except for a narrow band.

Another pitfall is underheating or overheating the plastic. When the plastic is bent before it has reached the proper temperature, its internal structure will be strained and small cracks, called crazing, may appear. At the other extreme, overheating may cause the plastic to bulge at the edges of the bend—although these protrusions can be ground down in the finishing process *(page 35)*.

A third pitfall is plastic's tendency to pick up the texture of the material against which it is formed. To prevent this kind of unwanted mimicry from occurring, the form can be covered with brown paper, felt or finely woven cloth.

Making a Simple Bend in Acrylic Sheet

1 Preparing the acrylic. Measure and mark the location of the bend line on the two edges of the plastic using a grease pencil. Measure out 35 mm on each side of these marks, then draw two pencil lines across the face of the acrylic, still covered with its protective masking paper. Score the masking paper lightly along the lines, using a dulled glass cutter so that you do not mar the surface of the acrylic *(left)*. Peel off the 70 mm strip of masking paper between the lines, along with its adhesive, and remove any traces of the adhesive with the recommended petroleum-based solvent *(page 47)*.

For a precise 90-degree angle, groove the bend line with a router *(page 27)*.

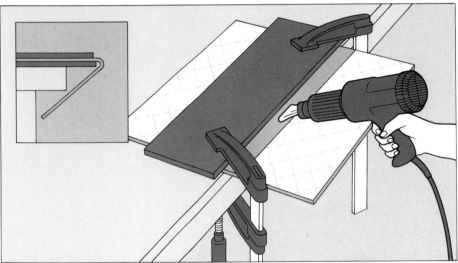

2 Heating the plastic. Position the two marks for the bend line directly over the straight edge of a worktop. Clamp over the acrylic a 100 mm-wide piece of 12 mm plywood with its front edge set back from the bend line by the thickness of the acrylic. Fit a spreader nozzle to a hot-air gun and set the temperature control, then direct the nozzle into the angle between the plywood and the acrylic and apply an evenly distributed stream of heat across the acrylic *(left)*. When the plastic begins to soften, bend down the acrylic sheet to the desired angle, and then another 5 degrees beyond.

For angles more acute than 90 degrees, create an extension of the worktop by placing a 12 mm plywood board under the acrylic and overlapping the worktop edge *(inset)*. To bend an acrylic sheet that has been grooved, heat the ungrooved side and bend the softened sheet only until the two faces of the V meet; overbending of the plastic is not necessary in this case.

Bending to a Precise Angle

Shaping over a form. To make a guide for a precise angle, position two equal-sized pieces of 3 mm plywood on a timber base to form a tent-like shape. Bevel the upper edges of the plywood and secure them with masking tape at the desired angle; drive panel pins or nails into the base to hold the bottom edges. Following the procedures described in Step 2, above, heat the acrylic and bend it about 5 degrees beyond the angle required, judging by eye; remove the plywood clamped to the acrylic, and allow the bend to retract. While the acrylic is still warm, position it over the plywood form and hold down its sides until the plastic has cooled—about a minute.

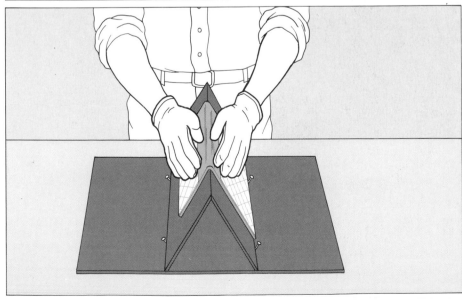

Bending Acrylic into Irregular Shapes

Forming the sheet. Soften the plastic in an oven, observing the precautions described on page 32. Wearing heat-resistant gloves, remove the plastic from the oven and bend it into the desired shape, working by eye or using a prepared form. For a cylindrical shape or a half-cylinder, hold the sheet over a large, empty can *(right)*, padding the can with felt to prevent the acrylic from mimicking irregularities.

For compound angles, such as those needed to form a lipped shelf, clamp the plastic between blocks and wedges *(top inset)*, keeping in mind that the corners of the blocks must be slightly bevelled to accommodate the plastic's rounded corners. For an undulating shape, clamp the plastic between the two matching halves of a wooden block that has been cut into a male-female mould *(bottom inset)*.

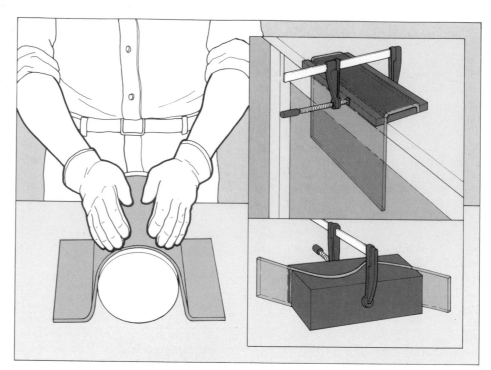

Bending PVC Pipe into Shape

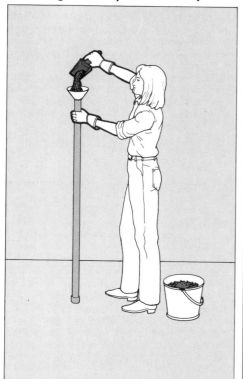

1 Filling the pipe with sand. Temporarily cap one end of the pipe with a PVC cap or several layers of aluminium foil secured with a rubber band, then pour sand into the other end with a funnel. When the pipe is filled, heat the area to be bent with a hot-air gun until it is pliable.

2 Bending the pipe. When the sand-filled pipe is flexible enough, bend it round a form or by hand. Allow for "memory" *(page 32)* by overbending as much as 20 per cent. The radius of the bend made in the pipe should not be less than 10 times the radius of the pipe itself.

Short or thin pipes can also be heated for bending by filling them with hot sand warmed in an old pan over low heat on a stove. To test whether the sand has reached the right temperature to make the PVC pliable, place a scrap of PVC in the pan while it is on the stove.

Giving Lustre and Polish to Edges and Surfaces

Most decorative plastics come fully polished, protected by paper masking. But unmasked edges must be smoothed, as must any cut or scratched surface.

This smoothing process consists of scraping, filing and sanding to remove rough edges and tool marks, followed by buffing and polishing to bring a high gloss to the surface. Not all surfaces need to receive the full treatment. The edges of a tabletop or a shelf should be buffed and polished until they are crystal clear, but edges that are to be glued or welded can simply be smoothed and left opaque.

The first step, scraping, applies in particular to hard plastics, such as acrylics and polycarbonates. A refinishing scraper is the most efficient tool, but you can improvise by grinding down an edge of a triangular file. Some of the softer plastics, such as polyvinyl chloride (PVC), can be smoothed with a block plane.

Along inside edges and round interior cutouts where a scraper cannot reach, filing is the principal finishing technique. Woodworking tools, such as smooth-cut rasps and bastard-cut mill files, are best for finishing edges; half-round, triangular and curved riffler files are useful for tight curves and fine details. A piece of chalk rubbed over the blade before use will stop the file from sticking.

Sanding, the next step in the smoothing process, is best done wet because the friction-caused heat of dry sanding can soften most thermoplastics. Steel wool can be substituted for abrasive paper.

Mechanical sanding with an orbital or a belt sander is faster and easier than hand sanding. To avoid heat build-up, keep the sander or the plastic in constant motion, avoid extreme pressure and frequently wet the surface being sanded.

Like sanding, buffing can be done either by hand or mechanically. To buff plastic by hand, use either a shoe buffer or a piece of soft flannel wrapped round a wooden block. When buffing irregular forms or curved surfaces, use a strip of flannel in the same way a shoeshine cloth is used. Buffing compounds of the type commonly used on metal are also suitable for plastic. They come in several grades, the finest of which are the coarsest you will usually need for working with plastics.

Mechanical buffing can be done on any kind of buffer. You can adapt a double-shafted bench grinder for buffing by substituting loose cotton buffing heads for the grinding wheels. For large sheets, use either a portable electric shoe buffer or an electric drill fitted with a buffing disc. Coat, or charge, the buffing head by holding a stick of buffing compound against the rotating wheel or disc until it is well covered with compound.

Any good-quality floor wax or car wax can be used to polish plastics, but plastics manufacturers often recommend specific compounds. These polishing pastes are applied in exactly the same manner as the buffing compounds.

In thermoplastics, such as polycarbonate and acrylic, drilled holes can be polished with methylene dichloride solvent, available in solvent-cementing kits *(page 46)*. The solvent, poured into the hole, works on the plastic by dissolving the thin frosty layer. This solvent can also be applied to the plastic with a cloth to smooth and polish the sides of a V-groove.

Shallow scratches on plastics can be polished out with white toothpaste. If the scratch is deep, sanding may be necessary, but because optical distortion may result, clear acrylic windows or skylights should be sanded carefully.

Abrasives Useful for Sanding and Buffing

Abrasive	Recommended coarseness			Comments
	Rough	Medium	Fine	
Sandpapers				
Garnet	100 grit	180 grit	280 grit	Durable.
Silicon carbide	80–100 grit	180–220 grit	330–600 grit	Fast-cutting, durable.
Tungsten carbide	36 grit	80 grit	150–200 grit	Very durable, can be cleaned with a wire brush or methylene dichloride solvent.
Steel wool	No. 0	No. 00–000	No. 000–0000	Can be used instead of sandpaper.
Buffing compounds				
Rouge	Finest grade only used with plastics.			Available in stick or cake form.
Tripoli	Finest grade only used with plastics.			Cuts slightly faster than rouge.

A full range of abrasives. Abrasive materials commonly used on plastics are listed in the column on the left. Listed to the right of each abrasive is the suitable range of grit or grain for rough sanding, semi-finishing and fine finishing. All of the sandpapers listed can be used wet, and for plastics they should be. When sanding a finished surface, start with the finest grade, or highest grit, paper so that the plastic will not be roughened more than necessary.

Step-by-Step Smoothing of Tool-Roughened Edges

1 **Scraping to remove saw marks.** Clamp the plastic in a vice, protecting the masked faces from damage by inserting scrap timber between the plastic and the vice jaws. Grasp the scraper with both hands and position it across the stock, tilting it back towards you at an angle of 60 degrees. Starting at the far end, drag the edge of the scraper over the length of the stock repeatedly, from back to front. Never push the blade forwards. Use moderate pressure and long strokes to avoid creating depressions in the piece.

2 **Wet sanding.** Fit a slab of plate glass or wood into one end of a shallow metal pan, and add water to a level just below the surface of the slab. Lay a full sheet of 100 grit wet and dry silicon carbide paper on the slab, grit side up, and wet the paper. Dip the plastic in the water and move the edge over the paper in an oval pattern. Keep the edge of the plastic flat on the paper and use even pressure. At frequent intervals, wet the plastic and rinse the abrasive paper.

When the surface is even and smooth, repeat the process with progressively finer grades of paper (*chart, page 35*) until the sanding marks are almost undetectable. Remove the fine dust by rinsing the plastic under running water.

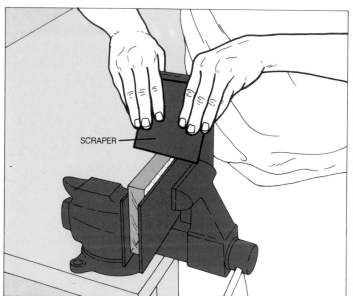

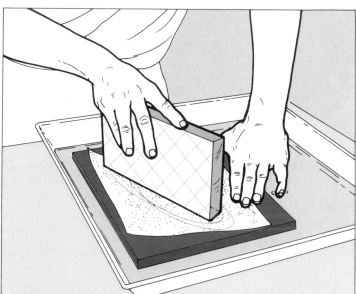

3 **Buffing and polishing.** To buff an edge, lift one end of the plastic against the bottom quarter of a buffing wheel coated with compound. Keep the stock in constant motion, moving it from side to side and up and down. Buff the edge up to its centre point, then reverse the work to buff the opposite end.

Wash the stock with soap and water to remove the abrasive buffing compound. Then polish the edge by coating the second buffing wheel with polishing paste or paste wax, and move the edge over the wheel, as above. Continue polishing until the edge is shiny, and then wipe the edge with a clean, soft cloth.

To buff and polish an edge by hand, clamp the plastic in a vice between protective timber scraps (*inset*), and use a sheepskin buffer coated with the same compound and wax as above; use separate buffing heads for the two operations. Hold the buffer flat against the edge and move it back and forth, parallel to the edge. Shift the position of the plastic often to smooth the edge evenly.

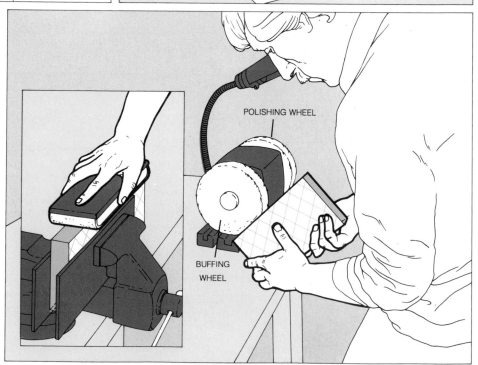

Smoothing and Buffing an Inside Curved Surface

1 Filing with a half-round file. Clamp the plastic in a vice between protective scraps of timber and, gripping a single-cut, half-round file with both hands, file across the plastic at right angles to the edge. Use light, even strokes and a forward motion, twisting the file a half-turn on each stroke. Rotate the plastic in the vice as needed to keep the surface that is being filed just above the jaws. Use a wire brush to clean the teeth of the file after every few strokes.

2 Sanding and buffing. Wrap a piece of 100 grit wet and dry paper round a dowel smaller in diameter than the curve to be sanded. Wet the sandpaper and the plastic with water, then sand with a combination back-and-forth and rolling motion, keeping the dowel level with the edge and working slowly round the circle. When the edge is fairly smooth, change to 240 grit, then to 400 grit paper. Rinse the plastic well with water each time you change the paper.

Replace the abrasive paper with felt. Coat the felt liberally with buffing compound and buff the edge, using the same technique as in sanding. Buff until smooth, then wash off the compound with soap and water.

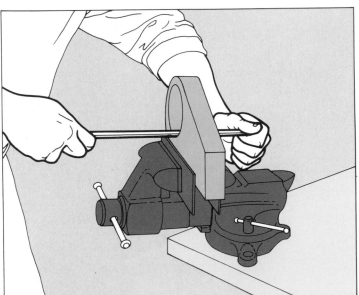

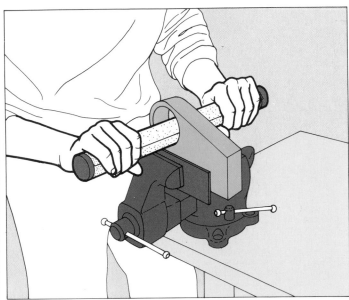

3 Polishing to a shine. Saturate a strip of lint-free cloth with polishing paste or paste wax. Holding the ends of the cloth firmly, draw it briskly back and forth over the surface. Polish until the surface shines, then repeat the procedure with a clean, dry piece of cloth.

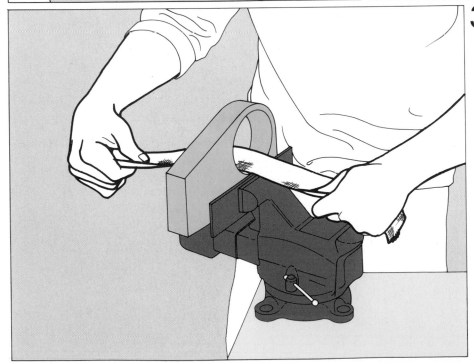

Removing a Scratch from an Acrylic Sheet

1 **Sanding the sheet.** Lay the plastic on a piece of felt on a flat work surface, and wet it with water. Using a sanding block and a fine-grade wet and dry sandpaper (approximately 280 grit for shallow scratches), sand very lightly in a star pattern. Keep the sheet and the sandpaper wet, and work over a wide area to avoid creating a noticeable depression in the plastic.

As the scratch disappears, use progressively finer grades of wet and dry paper in the same star pattern until the surface of the plastic is uniformly smooth. Wash off the dust with soap and water, and then dry the plastic with a damp chamois or paper towel.

2 **Buffing and polishing.** Use a portable electric drill fitted with a wool buffing disc, and coat the disc with buffing compound. Keeping the disc in constant motion, buff the sheet in small, overlapping loops until the sanding marks have disappeared and the stock is slightly shiny. Wash away the buffing compound, using your bare hands and soap and water.

Polish the sheet in the same manner as above, using a clean wool buffing disc, and either paste wax or polishing paste. When the sheet has the desired lustre, finish the job by hand-polishing it with a clean, dry cloth.

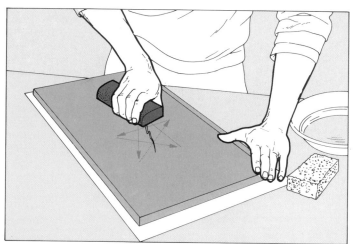

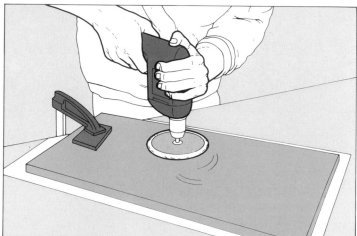

Two Ways to Polish a Small-Bore Hole

Using a drill stand. Cut a piece of wooden dowel, slightly longer than the depth of the hole to be polished and 3 mm smaller in diameter, and cut a 12 to 25 mm slit at one end. Slip a small piece of 280 grit wet and dry paper into the slit *(inset)* and tighten the dowel in the drill chuck. Clamp the plastic, supported by a piece of scrap timber, in the drill-stand table, centring the hole under the dowel. Squeeze a few drops of lubricating oil into the hole, then raise and lower the rotating dowel into the hole until the surface is smooth.

Clean the hole, then repeat the process, substituting a strip of felt, coated with buffing compound, for the sandpaper. Clean the hole again and repeat the process, using a new piece of felt coated with paste wax or polishing paste.

The same results can be accomplished by hand if you simply twist the dowel between your thumb and your forefinger, at the same time moving it slowly in and out of the hole.

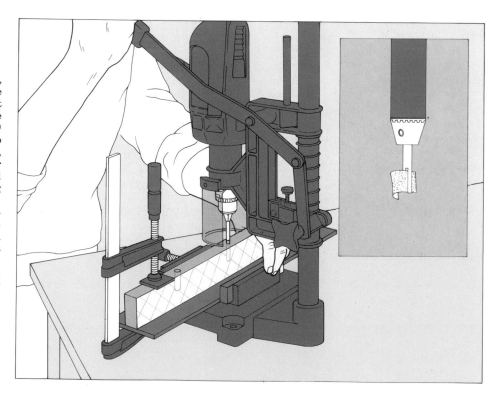

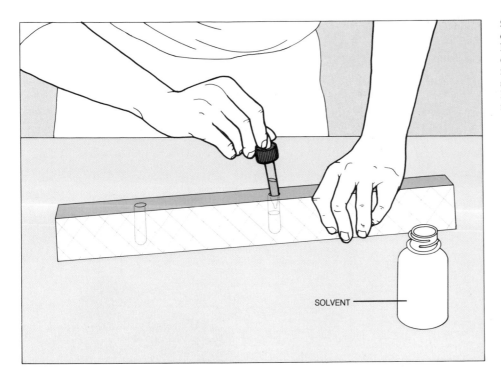

Solvent polishing. Knock any loose particles or dust from the hole. After ensuring good ventilation, hold the plastic upright and use a medicine dropper to fill the hole to the brim with methylene dichloride. Let the solvent work for 30 seconds, then pour it into a disposable container. Flush the hole immediately with soapy water; rinse with clear water.

SOLVENT

The Light Touch That Cleans Plastics

For all their toughness, plastics require a surprisingly gentle hand when it comes to maintenance. The thermoplastics—especially polystyrene, acrylic and polycarbonate—can be easily scratched, and because these plastics are usually clear, scratches caused by rough cleaning will be highly visible.

To remove superficial dirt from a thermoplastic, rinse the surface first with running water to rid the surface of any loose particles, which can scratch. Then wash with soap or a mild, non-abrasive detergent and water, using your bare hands or a soft cloth. Do not wipe the surface of the plastic with a completely dry cloth, since doing so can generate an electrostatic charge that will attract more dust and dirt.

Avoid abrasive scouring compounds, boiling water and harsh solvents such as acetone, benzene, toluene, carbon tetrachloride, and lacquer thinners—all of which will attack thermoplastics. So will many window-cleaning products. Isopropyl alcohol will remove the adhesive residue sometimes left by the paper masking on thermoplastic sheets. And if a solvent is needed to cut grease on these surfaces, use a good-quality paraffin. Remove the solvent immediately with soap and water, and dry the surface with a damp chamois. To remove yellowing from polycarbonates, wipe the area with butyl cellosolve and then repolish the surface with a polishing paste or paste wax, buffing it back to its original lustre with a soft cloth.

Thermosetting plastics, such as the laminates used on kitchen or bathroom surfaces, are not as sensitive as the thermoplastics are to solvents or abrasives, but they can be scratched with sharp objects and will discolour if subjected to high heat. Do not try to remove spots from thermosetting plastics with metal scrapers or scouring pads; wipe with a wet sponge and soap or a mild scouring compound. Polish with a clean cloth.

Glass-fibre-reinforced plastics have a tendency to craze, or develop fine surface cracks, when attacked by harsh solvents. Washing with detergent and water will remove most dirt; use isopropyl alcohol or paraffin when a solvent is needed to clean tough stains.

Welding a strong joint. An invisible jet of hot air from a thermal tool melts a PVC filler rod between the edges of two PVC sheets. The edges of the sheets have been bevelled to form a V-joint. The joint edges and the rod are simultaneously heated with an oscillating motion of the tip of the hot-air gun. As they soften, the rod is pushed gently into the joint, fusing the plastic surfaces. Several rods will be melted along the joint, overlapping each other until the V is filled.

The methods for joining one piece of plastic to another are both reassuringly familiar to and startlingly different from methods for joining metal and wood—a reflection of the chameleon nature of these synthetic substances. Many plastics can be joined with mechanical fasteners as prosaic as bolts and rivets; others with adhesives as mundane as PVA glue. But sometimes neither of these two standard fastening techniques is as effective or as convenient as one of several methods that are peculiar to plastics.

Two of these methods take advantage of plastics' most vexing weaknesses: their sensitivity to heat and to strong cleaning compounds. Many a home owner has discovered that polyethylene food wrapping instantly melts if brushed against a hot saucepan. But the same sensitivity to heat also makes it possible to weld plastics at temperatures far below those of conventional metal welding, using a hotplate or a household iron as a welding tool.

Similarly, the solvents in window-cleaning compounds that soften the surface of shatterproof plastic glass, causing it to haze and crack, also yield a method for creating an invisible joint. Used in small quantities and in confined areas, certain solvents soften two plastic edges so that, when pressed together, their molecules mingle and then harden into a firm molecular bond.

Not all of these fastening methods, familiar or unique, will work on all types of plastics. The world of synthetics is too varied. There are some plastics, especially thin films, that are too soft to accept mechanical fasteners; others, such as polyethylene, have slick, non-porous surfaces that reject adhesives, causing them to peel off. Still other plastics, notably the polystyrenes, char when heated, making hot-air welding impractical. Choosing the right technique becomes even more crucial in joining dissimilar plastics or in joining plastic and, say, wood.

Narrowing the choice still further are practical concerns. You will want to consider the conditions under which the assembled parts must perform. Must the joint be watertight or airtight? Solvent-cementing and welding are fine, but screws and rivets will not do. Must the joint be flexible enough to expand and contract with extreme temperature changes? Use a silicone adhesive and avoid PVA glue. Do looks count? The most attractive joint is produced by solvent cement, the least attractive by hot-air welding. But a welded joint is rugged. Will the parts need to be disassembled? Nuts and bolts are the logical choice. These and other considerations are discussed in the chapter that follows, making it possible for you to join plastic parts by the method that best suits the physical or aesthetic demands of the project.

Mechanical Devices: Joinery's Nuts and Bolts

The mechanical fasteners often used on plastics are the familiar screws, rivets, nuts and bolts that join wood and metal. Many of their applications are familiar too, but the unique properties of plastics allow for some variations on joinery techniques. Screws can be set into threads that have been heat-formed in thermoplastics; nuts can be embedded in plastic filler for a strong, invisible joint. Many plastics are

virtually friction-free, a property that makes them especially useful for simple smooth-swinging hinges in which ordinary long brads serve as hinge pins.

Rivets are the fasteners of choice for connecting thin sheets of plastic to each other or to non-plastic materials. Although they can be drilled out of their holes if necessary, rivets are best suited for permanent installations. They are also good for appli-

cations where vibrations might cause a threaded fastener to work loose. Screws or nuts and bolts provide greater strength than rivets and can be used with materials of any thickness. Most of these fasteners allow assemblies to be dismantled and reassembled repeatedly if required.

With any such fasteners, the physical characteristics of plastics give rise to other problems. Most plastics are not as strong as

Adapting Traditional Fasteners to New Uses

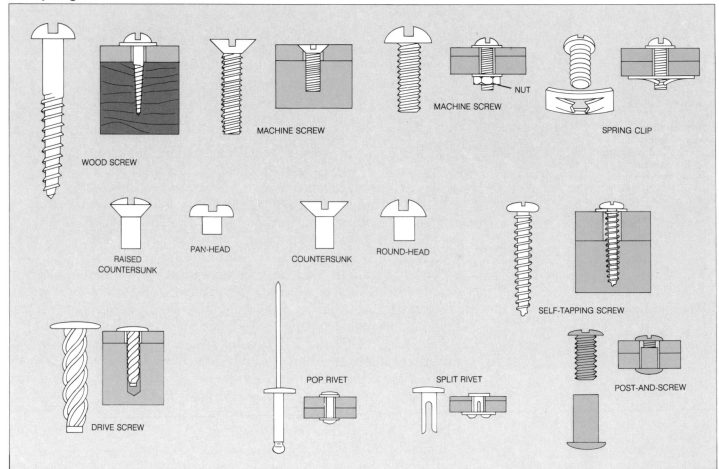

WOOD SCREW

MACHINE SCREW

MACHINE SCREW

NUT

SPRING CLIP

RAISED COUNTERSUNK

PAN-HEAD

COUNTERSUNK

ROUND-HEAD

SELF-TAPPING SCREW

DRIVE SCREW

POP RIVET

SPLIT RIVET

POST-AND-SCREW

Fasteners for every application. Wood screws are best suited for connecting plastic to wood, and they can be heated in order to form matching threaded holes in thermoplastics *(page 44)*. Machine screws can be used to attach plastic to any material, but they need a matched fitting: either a pre-threaded hole cut with a tap *(page 45)*, or a standard nut or a spring clip (which is pushed rather than threaded on to the screw). Both wood screws and machine screws are available with countersunk or raised countersunk heads that lie flush with the surface in countersunk holes, or

with round or pan heads that protrude above the surface and are generally used with washers to help distribute the pressure more evenly.

Self-tapping screws and drive screws, originally designed for metal, cut their own threads. Self-tapping screws carve their own path as the screwdriver turns; drive screws are forced into their holes by the pressure of hammer blows. Self-tapping screws can be used in both thermoplastics and thermosetting plastics. Drive screws, however, should be used only in thermoplastics, as they can easily cause cracks in the com-

paratively non-yielding thermosetting plastics.

Rivets can be used to join plastics to plastics or to other materials. Pop rivets are installed with a special tool that expands the tip of the rivet shaft into a head; split rivets are set by having their split ends bent outwards with a screwdriver. Both are inserted in pre-drilled holes and should be used with washers, to distribute pressure.

Combination post-and-screw fasteners can be used to join two pieces of plastic where little structural strength is required. The hole in each piece should be drilled to the diameter of the post.

wood or metal, so you must avoid excessive strain at any point. Tension on threads cut into plastic can strip the threads; tighten fasteners only until increased resistance is felt. Space fasteners closely to distribute strain evenly. To further distribute the pressure of each fastener, place a broad washer between the head of the fastener and the plastic itself.

Because most plastics are more responsive to temperature changes than other materials are, you must leave room for expansion and contraction when you attach a piece of plastic to another material at more than one point. If plastic is rigidly attached to wood, metal, glass or ceramic—all of them relatively stable materials—the plastic may split, crack or bow between the fastening points. To avoid problems of this kind, make the holes in the plastic larger than the fasteners, allowing the plastic to expand or contract in increments over its entire surface.

The slower expansion rates of the metal fasteners themselves can cause the expanding plastic to split or crack as it presses against the heads of the fasteners. You can prevent this happening by simply seating the nuts and bolts or rivets less tightly against the plastic.

Many of these problems can also be solved by using fasteners that are themselves made of plastic. Tough nylon screws with a variety of heads and the same characteristics as metal self-tapping screws react to heat and expansion in the same way as the materials they join. Plastic screws are particularly useful in situations where corrosion may be a factor.

Permanent Connections with Rivets and Washers

Quick fastening with pop rivets. Align the holes in the two pieces to be fastened, tapping them together if necessary. Insert the long mandrel of the rivet into the nosepiece of the pop-rivet tool, then insert the shaft of the rivet into the hole in the assembly. Place a back-up washer over the protruding shaft, and squeeze the handles of the pop-rivet tool together. Continue alternately squeezing and releasing the handles until the rivet is firmly seated and you feel increased resistance. Then squeeze the handles a final time to snap off the mandrel, leaving only the rivet head showing. If a nub of the mandrel protrudes, use a metal file to remove it.

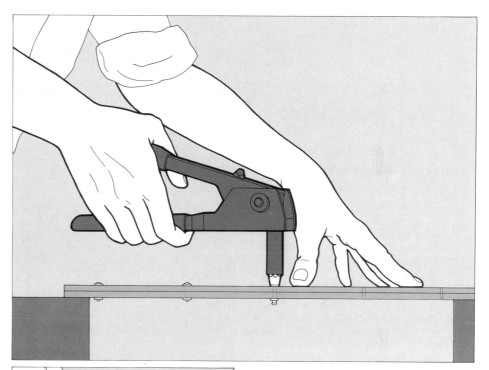

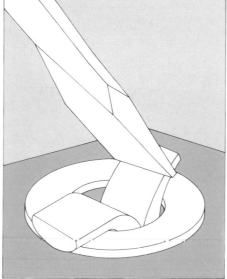

Installing a split rivet. Align the holes in the pieces to be joined, and insert a split rivet through them. Position the assembly, rivet head down, against a solid, padded surface, and slip a back-up washer over the split end of the rivet. With a screwdriver, bend each side of the rivet over the washer *(right)*. Then use long-nose pliers to curve the rivet ends back against the washer until the split rivet is snugly seated.

Hinging a Cover with a Pair of Pins

Making a pin hinge. Clamp or tape the movable piece into its closed position, and drill holes through the stationary pieces into both ends of the movable piece *(below, left)*. Position the holes along the same axis at each end of the assembly, and keep the drill bit aligned with that axis as you cut the two holes.

Remove the movable piece and slightly enlarge its two holes. Then reassemble the pieces and drive long, smooth wire brads into the holes *(below, right)*, using brads that fit snugly into the stationary piece.

Check the hinge assembly for free movement. File and sand away any plastic that interferes with the desired swing.

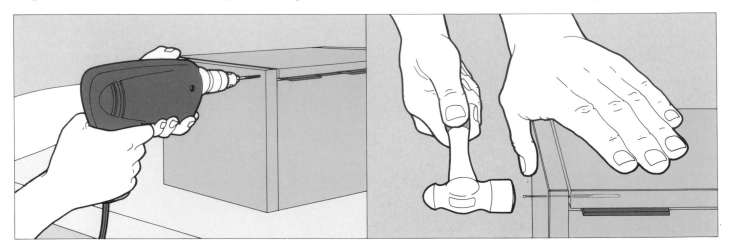

Thermoplastic Threads Formed by a Heated Screw

Shaping threads for a wood screw. Grip a new, clean wood screw firmly in a pair of pliers and then hold it over the flame of a butane torch *(right, above)* or a gas stove until it is deep blue. Then push it into a pre-drilled hole in the thermoplastic *(right, below)*; the hole should be slightly smaller in diameter than the outside thread of the screw, and as deep as the length of the screw. When the plastic has melted and cooled into the shape of the screw, remove the screw with a screwdriver. In the final assembly *(inset)*, use new screws of the same size.

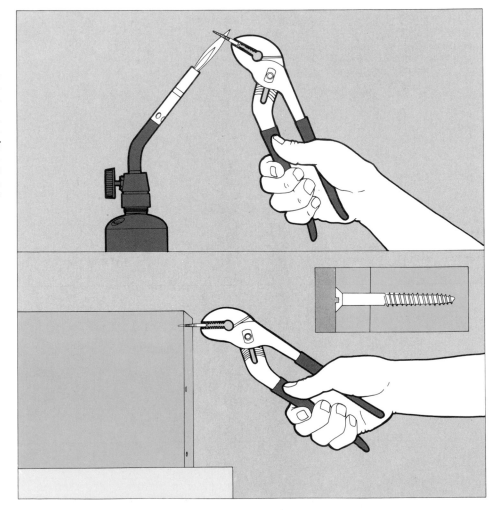

A Nut Sealed in Place for Extra Strength

1 **Installing the nut and bolt.** Drill a pilot hole for the bolt through the two pieces of plastic to be joined, making it the same size as the outside-thread diameter of the bolt. Counterbore the hole in what will be the finished surface, making it large enough for a washer and a nut with 3 mm of clearance. Drop in a washer, insert a bolt from below and thread a nut on to the bolt. Using a socket wrench to hold the nut, tighten the bolt until the pieces are firmly connected.

2 **Embedding the nut.** Using an oil can with a small spout, cover the threaded bolt end with a drop of light machine oil; in so far as possible, keep the oil off the nut. Mix a small batch of plastic patching compound *(page 103)* to match the colour of the plastic surface and pour it into the counter-sunk hole, filling the hole completely. Allow the patching compound to cure completely before removing the bolt from the nut, which will now be hidden in the patching compound.

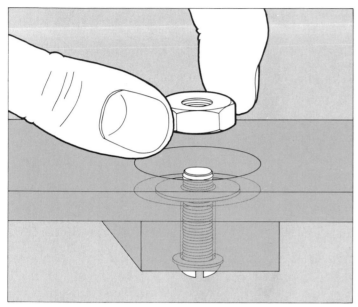

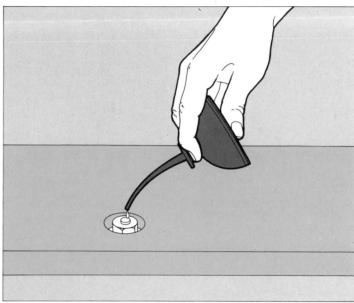

Threading a Hole with a Tap Wrench

Tapping threads in plastic. Mount a tap the size of the fastener in a tap wrench; dip the cutting threads in soapy water and, working clockwise, slowly begin to twist the tap into a pre-drilled hole in the plastic. Keep the tap exactly aligned with the hole, and back it out frequently to clear it of plastic chips.

When you drill the pilot hole, make its length equal to that of the chosen fastener and its diameter half way between the inside and outside diameters of the fastener's threads *(inset)*.

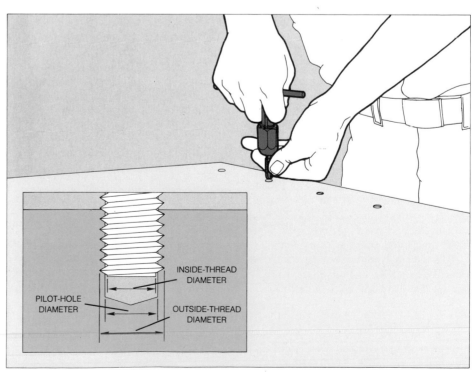

INSIDE-THREAD DIAMETER

PILOT-HOLE DIAMETER

OUTSIDE-THREAD DIAMETER

Parts Bonded with Cements, Glues or Solvents

Bonding is to plastic as screwing is to timber and welding to metal: it is the method of choice for assembling or repairing. Compared to screws, bolts or nails, bonding has the advantage of distributing the load it bears over the entire length of the joint. Compared to welding, it requires far simpler equipment—often no more than a fine brush for applying the adhesive and a jig to hold the bonded joint until it dries.

Plastics can be bonded using a wide variety of cements and glues, some of them familiar household products, others more esoteric (chart, opposite page). The type of plastic dictates the choice of adhesive, and for most plastics there is more than one choice. Two common plastics, however, polyethylene and polypropylene, are very difficult to cement-bond because of the waxiness of their surfaces, and they are best joined with heat.

The preferred method for bonding most of the hard, glass-like thermoplastics such as acrylic, polycarbonate, polystyrene and the cellulosics is solvent-cementing, a method peculiar to plastics. This technique takes advantage of the fact that these glassy plastics soften on contact with solvents. In the most common solvent-cementing process, the joint is assembled and then a few drops of solvent—usually methylene dichloride, either pure or in combination with other substances—are applied to the seam with a brush or a dispenser. Capillary action draws the solvent into the joint, where it softens the abutting edges. These then intermingle and, as the solvent evaporates, create a bond that is integral with the plastic.

In a variation of this technique, only one edge of the abutting plastics is softened, but it is softened to a greater depth, producing a slightly stronger joint. The edge is soaked in a pan containing a shallow layer of solvent. When the object is assembled, solvent from the soaked edge softens the adjacent surface; the edges melt, then harden into a strong bond.

Although solvent-cementing, with its crystal-clear joint, is most appropriate for joining furniture and kitchen or bathroom fixtures made of glass-like plastics, it is equally effective as a joining technique for other solvent-sensitive plastics, including polyvinyl chloride (PVC). The only precondition for its use is that the plastic parts must fit together without any gaps—since the amount of plastic softened is not enough to fill any unevenness. Square and sand the edges as described on pages 35–36, but do not polish them. If you are working with transparent plastic, a handy check for the precision of the joint is the water test shown opposite.

Acrylic can also be joined with a two-part acrylic cement. Useful for rough-trimmed edges and along joints that could benefit from the reinforcement of an extra fillet of material, it consists of a combination of acrylic resin and a hardener, mixed to a syrupy consistency just before use. Unlike solvent cement, acrylic cement actually requires a slightly open rather than a close-fitting joint; the opening is often produced by bevelling one of the edges of the joint to create a triangular crevice into which the cement is injected.

On plastics that cannot be bonded with either of these two special cements, many familiar adhesives work well. Objects cast from thermosetting resins can be bonded with epoxy cements; contact cements will fasten polyurethane foam; ordinary PVA adhesive is suitable for polystyrene foam.

Other common adhesives can be used on solvent-sensitive plastics when the neatness and clarity of a solvent-cemented joint are not crucial. Household cement will bond cellulosics; modelling glue joins polystyrene. These viscous plastic cements contain quantities of the specific plastic on which they can be used. Similar adhesives are available for PVC and for acrylic; they further extend the range of ways in which those materials can be joined.

When plastics are fastened to other materials, such as wood or metal, the range of possible adhesives broadens. Many such marriages require a pliant bond, to allow for the differing rates at which the two materials expand and shrink with temperature changes. Flexible epoxies—those without fillers—and adhesives based on silicone or synthetic rubber work best for such joints. PVA adhesive and viscous plastic cements join some plastics to porous materials, such as wood, and the so-called super glues lock plastics to a number of other materials.

Whatever bonding method you are to use, always observe certain preliminaries. First, read the label on the adhesive container. Not only will the label verify that you have selected the best product for the job, but it will also provide storage and use instructions and alert you to curing times—how long the joint must be immobilized before it is ready for use.

Make sure, too, that the surfaces to be bonded are clean—free of grease, polishing paste and traces of adhesive from the masking paper. To clean glass-like thermoplastics, wipe with a lint-free cloth or chamois moistened in isopropyl alcohol. Objects cast from thermosetting resins such as epoxy and polyester must often be sanded to remove mould-release compound and to roughen their surfaces for better adhesion. Finally, design the joint and the clamping set-up before you begin to apply the cement. Most adhesives give you very little time to reconsider, and firm, steady clamping is essential in making a strong joint. Do not, however, clamp joints too tightly; this can cause stresses that will weaken the joints.

Because the fumes of plastic solvents, cements and glues are often inflammable and nearly always irritating, safety guidelines similar to those for liquid plastics (page 8) must be followed assiduously. Always work in a well-ventilated area. Take large jobs outdoors—but wait for warm weather; many cements cure slowly and form a weak joint at low temperatures. Do not leave cement and solvent containers open any longer than necessary, and avoid extended skin contact with any cement or solvent. Never use any of these substances after drinking alcoholic beverages (the fumes may combine dangerously with the alcohol), near an open flame, or while smoking.

A Guide to Choosing the Right Adhesive

Plastics	Bonded to:			
	Itself	Reinforced plastics	Wood	Metal
ABS	Solvent	Contact adhesive	Epoxy cement	Epoxy cement
Acrylic	Solvent, thickened acrylic cement, two-part acrylic cement	Two-part acrylic cement	Two-part acrylic cement	Contact adhesive
Cellulosics	Solvent, household adhesive	Contact adhesive	Household adhesive	Contact adhesive
Polycarbonate	Solvent, thickened polycarbonate cement	Contact adhesive	Epoxy cement	Epoxy cement
Polystyrene	PVA adhesive	PVA adhesive	PVA adhesive	Super glue
Polystyrene foam	PVA adhesive	PVA adhesive	PVA adhesive, contact adhesive	Epoxy cement
Polyurethane foam	Contact adhesive	Epoxy cement, contact adhesive	Contact adhesive	Contact adhesive
PVC	Solvent, thickened PVC cement	Contact adhesive	Contact adhesive	Contact adhesive
Rigid thermosetting plastics (phenolics, epoxies, polyester, melamine)	Epoxy cement	Epoxy cement	Contact adhesive	Epoxy cement, contact adhesive

Fitting the adhesive to the job. In the chart above, the first column lists the plastics most commonly fastened with cements or glues. The other four columns list the preferred bonding agents for joining them to the materials at the top of the columns. Three of the materials—reinforced plastics, wood and metal—account for the majority of surfaces to which small plastic parts are joined in building or assembling larger objects. If the chart lists more than one bonding agent, all are equally effective. Appearance or clamping requirements may affect the choice—a fast-setting adhesive is often preferable for a complex joint, which may be difficult to clamp.

The bonding agents are identified by their generic names. Since they are sold in various forms and under various trade names, you will have to check the ingredients—read the packet label or ask the supplier to be sure that you are getting the cement or glue you want. Most of these bonding agents are available at hardware shops, and household adhesive is, of course, available everywhere. Special solvent and two-part cements are also sold at hardware or D.I.Y. shops.

A Water Test to Verify That Edges Fit Precisely

Locating surface irregularities. When you are joining clear plastics with solvent cement, a method requiring perfectly matched surfaces, dribble a few drops of water from a medicine dropper on to one face of the joint. Assemble the joint, then sight through the plastic to watch the behaviour of the water. If it spreads in an even film throughout the joint, the joint is ready for cementing. But if water puddles in some areas *(inset)*, the edges require further smoothing. Continue to file, scrape and sand the unpuddled areas, repeating the water test from time to time. Be sure to dry before cementing.

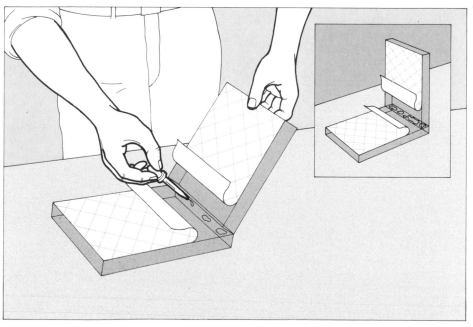

Solvent-Softened Edges
to Hold a Butt Joint

1 **Assembling and immobilizing the joint.** Butt together the pieces of plastic being joined, and anchor them at 75 or 100 mm intervals with lengths of masking tape stretched taut. Then carefully lift the taped plastic pieces and turn them over, propping them slightly above the work surface on wooden blocks spaced to give clearance to the seam. Brace the top with additional wooden blocks to immobilize the joint and prevent the pieces of plastic from bulging upwards because of the tension of the tape.

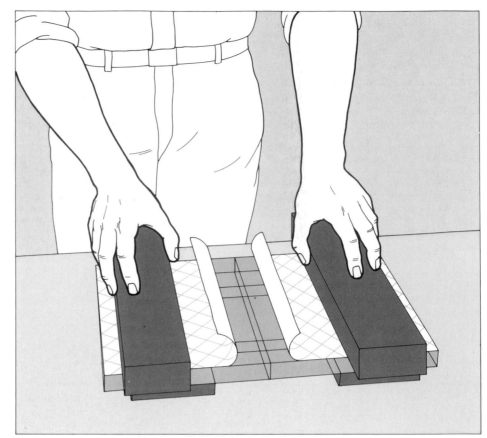

2 **Applying the solvent.** Wearing a respirator, dip a very fine artist's brush in the container of solvent, taking care to wet only the bristles so the solvent does not attack the finish of the handle. Blot the brush on the lip of the container; then draw the brush along the joint, stopping to reload the brush if it becomes dry. Do not allow excess solvent to pool on the surface of the plastic. Capillary action will draw the solvent into the narrow aperture of the joint as you apply it. If the joint shows light-coloured areas, an indication that the solvent has not penetrated the joint completely, make a second pass with the brush.

Let the joint stand undisturbed for at least 15 minutes. Wait at least four hours before putting any weight on the joint and before sawing, drilling or sanding in its vicinity.

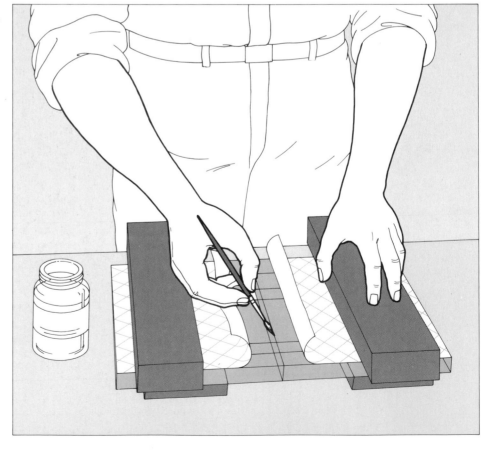

Using a Jig for Cementing a Corner Joint

1 **Aligning and anchoring the joint.** Make a right-angled jig from two pieces of 20 mm timber, one of which has been rebated to form a channel at the inside apex of the angle; nail the jig together. Position the plastic pieces in the jig so that the seam falls over the channel; this will prevent excess solvent from pooling between the wood and the plastic, blemishing the plastic. When the joint is properly aligned, secure the plastic with masking tape, as shown below, or with spring clips or large rubber bands.

2 **Filling the joint with solvent.** Using a fine artist's brush or the needle-thin applicator nozzle of a solvent-cementing kit, dispense an even flow of solvent along the length of the joint. If capillary action fails to draw enough solvent into the seam to fill it, make a second pass, adding another bead of solvent. Wait at least 15 minutes before removing the plastic from the jig, and at least four hours before subjecting the bonded joint to stress of any kind.

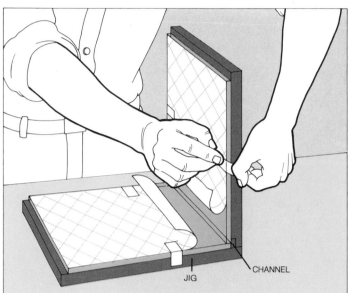

JIG

CHANNEL

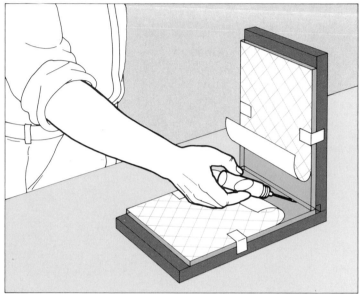

A Solvent Dip to Soften Parts for Joining

1 **Softening one edge in solvent.** Working in a well-ventilated area, prepare the dipping bath by arranging a pattern of paper-clip supports in the bottom of an aluminium or glass baking dish; the pattern of paper clips should match the outline of the edge being softened—in this example, a plastic cylinder. Pour just enough solvent into the dish to cover the paper clips, and set the plastic on top of them; only the bottom edge of the plastic should be in contact with the solvent. Leave the plastic in the solvent for six to eight minutes, so that the edge can soften.

To slow the evaporation of dangerous vapours during the dipping operation, use the smallest dish possible. For extra protection, you can make a cover for the dish from polyethylene film. Cut a hole in the cover just large enough to accommodate the plastic being softened, and tape the cover to the sides of the dish.

2 **Assembling the joint.** Remove the film and lift the plastic from the dipping bath, tilting the plastic so that any remaining solvent collects at one point on the edge, then blotting away the excess. Align the two parts being joined—in this example, a cylinder and circular base. Allow the assembly to sit undisturbed for a minute or two, while the solvent spreads from one piece of plastic to the other. Then weight or clamp the assembly for an hour; do not put any stress on the joint for at least 24 hours.

As soon as you remove the plastic from the dipping bath, cover the bath with a metal sheet or a piece of polyethylene film, to slow evaporation of the solvent. The bath can be reused for additional joints, or discarded.

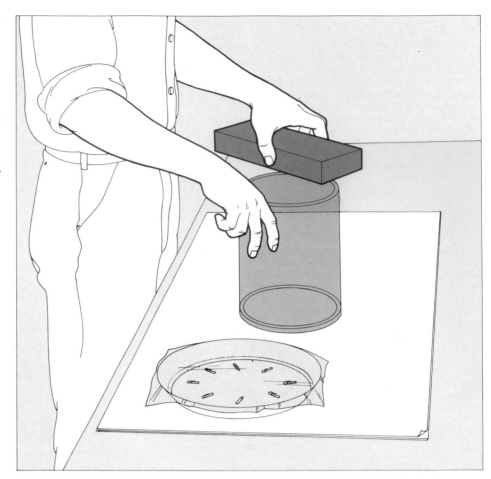

Mistakes to Avoid in Solvent-Cemented Joints

Three failed joints. A poor fit between the pieces in the joint on the left caused an incomplete bond; because the solvent could not spread evenly throughout the joint, the seam is weak and unattractively blotchy. To avoid such problems, always be sure to scrape away any saw marks and sand the edges carefully before assembling any solvent-cemented joint.

The bulging joint in the centre was caused by premature clamping. The solvent in the dipped edge did not have time to soften the adjacent plastic; the pressure of the clamp against the still-hard plastic therefore squeezed the tacky material out of the joint.

The fine cracks that mar the curved plastic surface, above right, were produced when solvent was inadvertently spattered on the curved surface. The curved plastic, already stressed by heat-bending, was further weakened by the solvent, and the accumulated strains caused the web of cracks, called crazing. To reduce the chances of crazing, allow only the edge of the plastic to touch the dipping bath, and remove as little as possible of any protective masking paper.

Strong Acrylic Joints with a Two-Part Cement

Mixing the resin and hardener. Allow both the resin and the hardener to reach room temperature, then pour the resin into a disposable cup or polyethylene container and add the prescribed amount of hardener, following the proportions listed on the label. Stir the mixture gently but thoroughly with a wooden spatula for a minute or two, taking care not to introduce bubbles. If air bubbles do appear, let the mixture stand for three to five minutes, until the bubbles rise to the surface and are dispersed.

Working quickly—the syrupy mixture will harden to uselessness in about 25 minutes—fill the disposable applicator by dipping the tip in the mixture and slowly pulling up the plunger. When you have finished with the cement, allow the leftover mixture to harden before discarding both the container and the applicator.

Acrylic-cementing a butt joint. Bevel the edge of one piece of plastic to an angle of 15 degrees, as described on page 24, then butt the two pieces of plastic together, bevelled edge up in the joint. Weight the plastic between wooden blocks as shown in Steps 1 and 2, page 48. Leave a 1 mm gap between the two plastic edges to be joined and secure the underside of the gap with a temporary masking-tape seal.

To construct the seal, cut a strip of 25 mm masking tape slightly longer than the joint, and a strip of 12 mm masking tape, also slightly longer than the joint. Place the 12 mm strip down the centre of the 25 mm strip, sticky sides together *(inset)*, and attach the seal to the plastic. Lap the tape over the ends of the joint to form dams for the cement. The sticky margins will seal the joint, and the centre strip will prevent the adhesive on the tape from interfering with the curing of the cement.

Beginning at one end of the joint, fill the joint groove with cement by depressing the plunger of the applicator and moving it back and forth along the joint; overfill the groove slightly, to allow for shrinkage as the cement cures. Let the joint stand undisturbed for at least four hours. After 24 hours, sand the bead of cement level with the plastic surface *(pages 35–37)*.

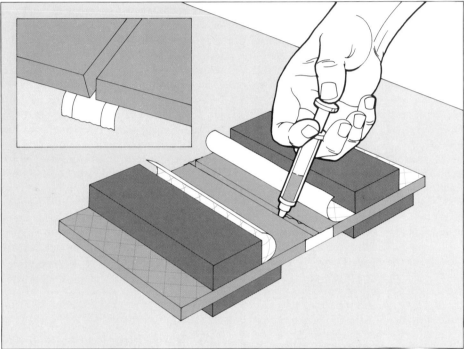

Acrylic-cementing a right-angled joint. Nail together two pieces of 20 mm timber to form a right-angled jig; trim the outside edge of the jig's joint at a diagonal, forming a chamfered corner. Bevel the edge of one piece of plastic to an angle of 15 degrees, and tape or clamp the two pieces of plastic against the outside of the jig. Position the unbevelled piece flat against the work surface and set the bevelled piece against it, bevel facing out and 6 mm back from the edge of the unbevelled piece; this 6 mm ledge will be removed at a later stage.

Using the applicator, dispense a bead of cement into a grooved joint, overfilling it slightly to allow for shrinkage. While the cement is still viscous, shape it into a concave fillet with the tip of the syringe. Allow the joint to cure for four hours; then, for a stronger bond, make a second fillet on the inside of the joint. After 24 hours, use a table saw *(page 24)* and a medium mill-cut metal file *(pages 35–37)* to trim off the 6 mm ledge, leaving a smooth right angle.

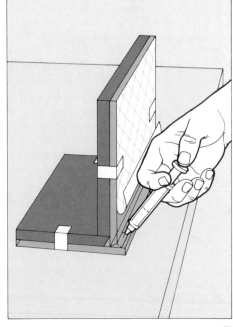

Heat as a Means of Merging Thermoplastics

Because of the low melting point of many thermoplastics, welding them with heat produces none of the showy pyrotechnics of metal welding. Nor does it require the same kind of heavy equipment. But like metal welding, joining plastic by means of heat produces a bond that is waterproof, airtight and, in some cases, the joint thus made is fully as strong as the non-welded areas of the material.

Virtually any of the thermoplastics can be welded. Thermosetting plastics, on the other hand, merely char or decompose if they are subjected to welding heat. The plastics that are most commonly welded are polyethylene, polypropylene and polyvinyl chloride (PVC). Polyethylene and polypropylene resist solvents and therefore cannot be joined with solvent cement *(pages 48–50)*—a generally swifter and neater technique. Lengths of PVC pipe are joined with solvent cement, but the heat-welding process produces stronger joints in PVC sheet and film. Nylon, which can be cemented only after special surface preparation, is very often welded instead.

Like metal welding, plastic welding requires that the edges of parts be heated to a liquid and then held together until the molten material fuses and sets. Because the strength of a welded joint depends on molecular fusion—the uniform comingling and coalescence of the materials that are being joined together—it is only identical thermoplastics that can be successfully welded to each other.

The amount of heat that is needed to accomplish the necessary fusion—and the length of time that the plastic must be subjected to it—vary with the thickness and type of the plastic you are using. Most plastics can be sufficiently liquefied in less than half a minute at temperatures ranging from 220 to 295°C. Because these temperatures are relatively low, the heat for plastics welding can be generated by almost any heating tool or appliance—including a household iron or a cooking hob. However, plastics welding is also done with certain specialized tools, such as hot-air welding guns *(pages 56–60)*.

The handiest tool for heating the ends of pipes, rods and small sheets of plastic is a hotplate—preferably one with a thermostatic control and a smooth aluminium or steel top. To stop the plastic from sticking to the plate, coat it with Teflon spray. Never use wax, oil or silicone on the hotplate; they can be picked up by the plastic and will fatally weaken any weld being made. For the same reason, be sure to clean any excess melted plastic off the hotplate after each use, either by carefully wiping it with a rag while it is still hot or by scraping it off with a knife or a razor blade after it has cooled and hardened.

To melt the ends of small parts, heat can be most precisely applied with a hot scrap of metal. Commonly, a small piece of aluminium or steel sheet is heated on a hotplate, or with a propane torch, and then touched briefly to the parts of the plastic to be melted. Of course, the open flame itself must never come into contact with the plastic—the material would ignite rather than melt. For the flexible seams that are needed to join thin plastic sheets or films, an ordinary household iron performs admirably *(page 63)*.

No matter which heating method you use, plastic edges to be joined must be scrupulously clean and must be cut to fit each other precisely. Then, to maintain the precise fit, the joint should be aligned with a jig as it cools.

A simple two-part jig for flat or round objects can be made from two pairs of timber or plywood strips, each pair nailed together at a 90-degree angle to form an L-shaped support *(Step 2, opposite page)*. The two parts of the jig are secured about 25 mm apart on a timber or plywood base and the plastic sections being joined are seated in them, with the seam line in the open space between. The two-part jig aligns the joint and also supports the plastic sections while the weld is cooling.

A more complex two-part jig that is used for precise alignment of small rods and tubing is mounted on the jaws of a vice; as the jaws of this jig are closed, the cylindrical pieces of plastic are moved smoothly together *(page 55)*.

Because of the low temperatures involved, most plastics welding can be safely done in any room of the house. The worktable can be protected with a sheet of cardboard or plywood. But good ventilation is essential. Any plastic, when melted, gives off noxious fumes, and the fumes of PVC can be extremely harmful. If welding PVC, use a fan or two to disperse fumes; avoid leaning close to the work, where vapours are most concentrated.

The Handy Hotplate for Minor Welding

1 Melting the edges. Set a thermostatically controlled hotplate to a temperature of about 260°C. Hold the pieces of plastic that you will be welding against the plate, at right angles to its surface, without applying any pressure.

When the lower edges of the plastic become clear and pliable about 3 mm up from the surface of the hotplate, the thin layer of plastic that is in direct contact with the plate will be liquid and ready for joining.

2 **Joining the pieces.** Lift the two pieces of plastic straight up from the hotplate and place them in the two-part jig, butting them against the jig's L-shaped back *(below, left)*. Immediately slide them towards each other until their molten surfaces touch. Press them together just enough to form a small bead of plastic along the joint *(inset)*. Hold the pieces in position until the plastic cools. Then smooth off the bead with 280 to 400 grit wet abrasive paper or a sharp knife.

When you are fusing pipes and rods *(below, right)*, hold them in alignment by pushing them into the right angle formed by the bottom and the back of the jig.

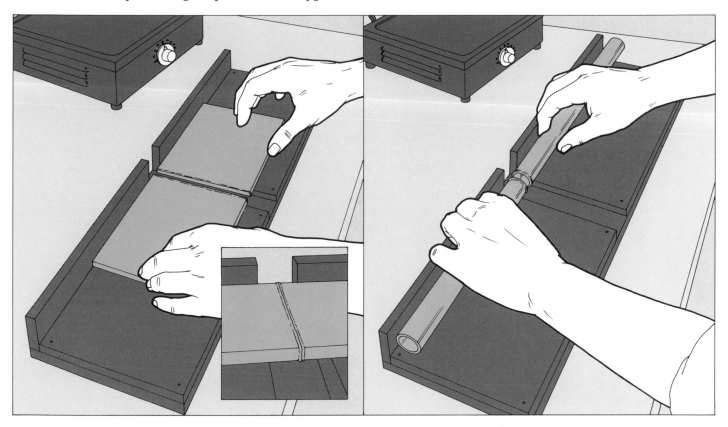

A Double-Faced Heater Made of Scrap Metal

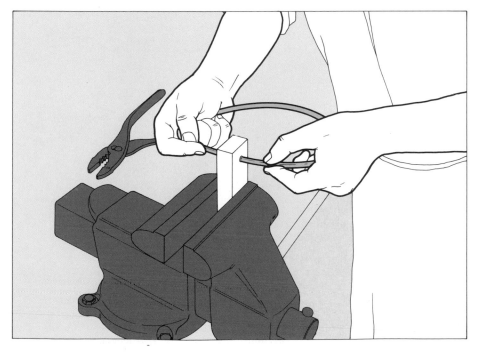

1 **Melting the plastic.** Heat a small scrap of aluminium or steel on a hotplate or over a gas flame. Using pliers, lift the hot metal and clamp it between the jaws of a vice. Touch the two pieces of plastic to opposite sides of the metal, holding them there until they soften and become clear to a depth of approximately 3 mm.

2 **Fusing the parts.** Pull the melted ends of the plastic straight out from the heated metal—without letting them slide—and quickly press them together firmly enough to form a slight bead at the joint. Hold the plastic until it cools and hardens. Remove the bead as in Step 2, page 53.

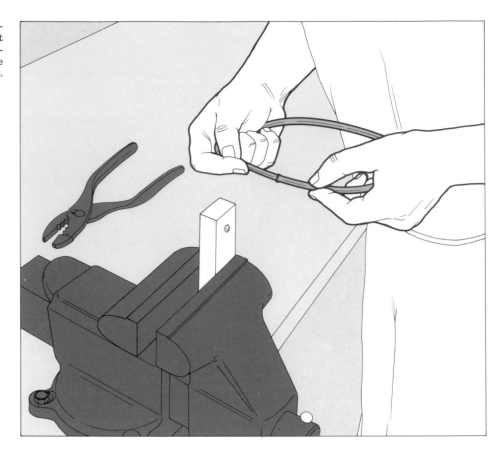

A Jig Designed to Align Parts Being Welded

1 **Constructing the jig.** Cut two pieces of 50 by 25 mm timber the same length as the jaws of the vice. Drill two small holes edgewise across each piece for a bolt-and-wing-nut assembly, positioning the holes about 25 mm from the ends of the wood; countersink the holes. Then drill a large hole through the face of each piece of timber, centring it exactly; make the diameter of the hole the same size as, or slightly smaller than, that of the plastic tubing or rod being joined.

Cut a saw kerf, 9 mm deep and 6 mm in from the edge, into each end of the timber to provide a slot for a jubilee clip. Then cut each piece of timber in half lengthwise, dividing the large hole into a pair of semicircles.

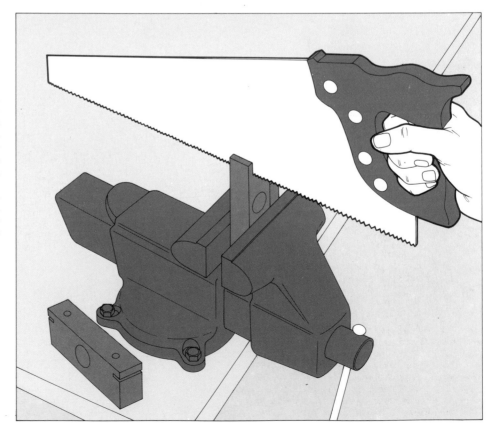

2 Mounting the jig. Insert bolts through the bolt holes in the upper and lower halves of the jig sections, securing them with wing nuts. Loop a jubilee clip through each saw kerf, and attach the two jig sections to the two jaws of the vice. Then loosen the wing nuts, and clamp a length of plastic tubing or rod in each of the two jig sections. Finally, loosen the jubilee clips and adjust the positions of the jig parts until the ends of the plastic are perfectly aligned; tighten the clips.

Joining Rods or Tubes in a Jig-Equipped Vice

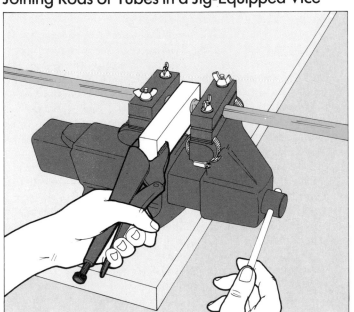

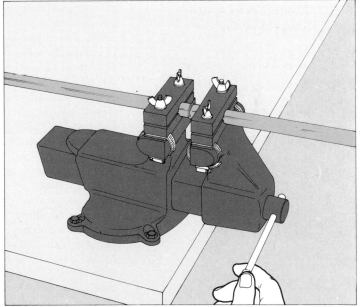

1 Melting the jig-held plastic. Open the jaws of the vice until the ends of the tubing or rod are about 20 mm apart. Then insert a piece of scrap metal, heated as in Step 1, page 53, between the ends of the plastic, and tighten the vice until the ends rest against the hot metal. Leave the metal held firmly in place until the plastic is soft and clear to a depth of about 3 mm.

2 Fusing the ends of the plastic. Open the vice just enough to free the softened ends of the plastic from the hot metal. Remove the metal and immediately close the vice, bringing the ends of the plastic together; apply just enough pressure to form a small bead of plastic at the joint. Let the plastic cool and harden, then remove it. Smooth off the bead as in Step 2, page 53.

Welding Plastics with a Torch

A welding torch, originally designed for industrial uses such as repairing plastic ductwork and storage tanks, makes short work of household repairs such as joining the broken plastic blades of a fan, patching a hole in a water storage tank, or joining sheets of flexible plastic for lining ornamental fishponds. Although many of the same tasks can be performed with a hot-air gun *(page 32)*, a welding torch is designed specifically for the job and affords more exact heat control. The torch directs a jet of hot air over a plastic filler rod and the joint being filled; as the surfaces soften, they fuse together to produce a joint as strong as the plastic itself and far stronger than a joint made with solvent or adhesive.

The end of a welding torch contains a powerful heating element over which hot air is blown. The air exits through one of several interchangeable nozzles that can spread or concentrate the stream of air, as the particular weld requires. Portable and reasonably priced welding torches suitable for D.I.Y. use can be bought in hardware shops or from specialist plastics suppliers.

Welding temperatures must be varied from as high as 600°C to as low as 220°C according to the type of plastic. At too low a temperature the plastic will not melt, while at too high a temperature the surface of the plastic will char or burn. The easiest plastics to weld are those with the widest melting range, such as PVC and polypropylene. Before undertaking a weld it is wise to practise on a piece of plastic of the same sort as that to be welded, adjusting the heat of the air flow as necessary to obtain a good result.

Although there are many ways to make a welded plastic joint, good preparation of the plastic and a good welding technique are essential. Clean the edges of the plastic thoroughly and roughen them with sandpaper or a file. To start the weld, position the pieces carefully and, if necessary, hold them together with a push stick or cramps; then use a tacking nozzle to secure the joint temporarily *(page 58)*.

The filler rod for the weld must be the same type of plastic as that being welded. You can use a strip cut from a plastic sheet, but extruded round and triangular rods, available in rolls of several sizes and lengths, are more convenient. When melting the rod into the joint, hold the welding nozzle about 10 mm from the plastic and move it back and forth in a fanning motion to distribute heat evenly on to the filler rod and joint. Heat the rod only enough to liquefy its surface; its core should remain stiff enough to be pushed into the joint. Depending on the thickness of the stock you are welding, several rods may have to be laid in to fill the joint.

A slightly different welding technique is used for speed welding, a variant process that is particularly useful for projects involving many joints. In speed welding, a special type of slotted welding tip dispenses heated filler rod or filler strip directly on to the joint. This eliminates the need to fan the tip over the filler in order to heat it evenly. Also, because it is in effect one-handed welding, freeing one hand to hold the plastic in position, the weld can often be made without any preliminary clamping and tacking.

Whatever the welding mode employed, joining plastics with heat is generally a safe procedure. Except at the end of the welding tip, the temperatures involved are moderate; no special protective clothing or gear is required, and the work surface needs no special insulation. Do not, however, aim the tip at your skin at close range. Also, be sure that the welding area is well ventilated: melting plastics release noxious fumes; those of PVC are particularly dangerous to inhale.

If you are changing nozzles in the middle of a welding operation, remember that the nozzle you are replacing will have retained a considerable amount of heat, so handle it with pliers. After completing the weld, switch off the heating element and allow cold air to pass over it—this prevents the element from burning out prematurely.

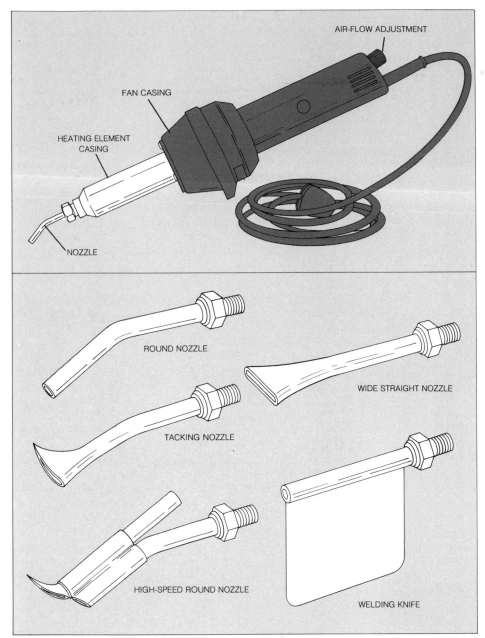

A welding torch with a choice of nozzles. When the torch is plugged in and switched on, air is drawn in at the rear by an internal fan and passed over a heating element before it exits from the front of the torch through a nozzle. On the model shown, temperature is adjusted by altering the speed of the air flow from the fan—at a low setting the air passes over the heating element more slowly and comes out hotter than at a high flow setting. On more sophisticated types of welding torch, the temperature of the heating element can also be adjusted.

By shaping and directing the emission of air in various ways, different nozzles increase the versatility of the welding torch. The tacking nozzle, for spot welding a joint to hold it in place temporarily, has a sharply protruding end that focuses hot air on to the plastic join. The all-purpose round nozzle, which is appropriate for most welding tasks, delivers a broader, more uniform flow than the tacking nozzle does. The wide, straight nozzle spreads the air flow for welding, for example, flexible plastic sheet. The high-speed round nozzle, designed for speed welding, lays softened lengths of rod directly into the joint. The welding knife, a Teflon-coated metal flange that is heated by the hot air flowing through the duct at the top, can be used for butt-welding small parts *(page 53)* or for sealing film *(page 64)*.

AIR-FLOW ADJUSTMENT

FAN CASING

HEATING ELEMENT CASING

NOZZLE

ROUND NOZZLE

TACKING NOZZLE

WIDE STRAIGHT NOZZLE

HIGH-SPEED ROUND NOZZLE

WELDING KNIFE

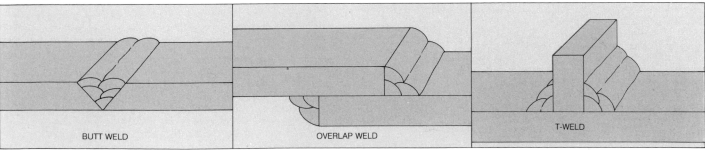

BUTT WELD

OVERLAP WELD

T-WELD

Three basic welds. For a butt weld *(above, left)*— the commonest way to join two pieces of plastic end to end—the edges of the joint are bevelled at a 30-degree angle, creating a 60-degree V-groove. A 0.5 mm space at the bottom of the groove allows the molten plastic to penetrate the joint, and one or more filler rods are laid into the groove.

For an overlap weld *(above, centre)*, often used in patching large holes, one piece of plastic is laid on top of another, and the right angles where they meet are filled with molten plastic.

For a corner weld, layers of filler are similarly laid into the right angle formed by the two pieces of plastic. For a stronger corner weld, butt the two pieces of plastic together in a T and weld on both sides *(above, right)*; the excess plastic on the outside of the T is then trimmed back to the edge of the melted filler rods reinforcing the joint.

Judging weld quality. The three butt welds illustrated show the effect on a joint of differing amounts of heat. In the weld right, above, the filler rod has not been heated enough to lose its shape and has fused incompletely. Correct this defect before adding any more filler rod; reheat the weld, and either move the welding tip more slowly along the joint or increase the heat of the air leaving the nozzle. The gently rounded top of the filler material in the weld far right, above, indicates that just enough heat was used to fuse the rods to each other and the sides of the joint, creating a strong bond. In the discoloured weld right, below, either the tip was moved too slowly or the air temperature was too high: the filler rod overheated and charred before it could fuse. This joint cannot be salvaged; cut away the burned material and replace it with new filler rod.

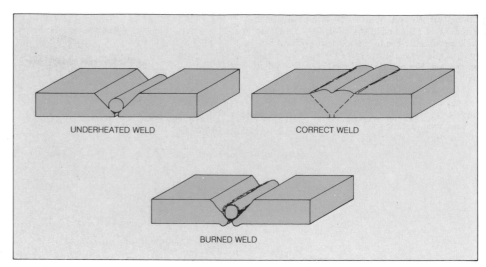

UNDERHEATED WELD   CORRECT WELD

BURNED WELD

Using a Filler Rod to Seal a Butt Joint

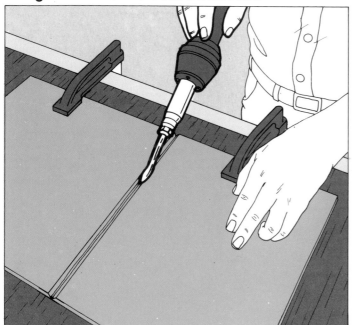

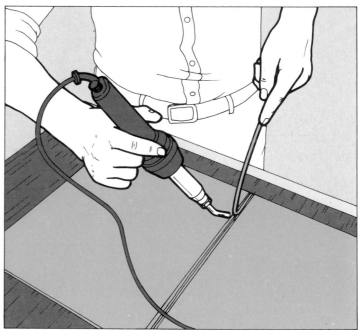

1 Setting up the weld. Place a piece of plywood on the work surface to help the plastic retain heat during welding. File or sand the two edges to be joined to 30-degree angles and butt them together, with a hairline gap at the bottom of the V; clamp the plastic to the plywood. Fit a tacking nozzle into the torch and turn on the heat; let the nozzle warm up for two minutes. Hold the torch so the nozzle is in contact with the plastic at the join and at an angle of 45 degrees to the seam. Draw the tip along the seam with a gentle pressure at a speed of 750 to 1000 mm a minute.

2 Welding the joint. Replace the tacking nozzle with a round nozzle, using pliers to remove the tacking nozzle if it is still hot. Allow the new nozzle to heat up; then, holding the torch in one hand and a filler rod in the other, set the rod in the groove at one end of the joint. Holding the nozzle above the rod, move the nozzle back and forth in a fanning motion across the joint, so that both the rod and the edges of the groove melt equally. As the rod melts, push it gently down into the groove. Move the torch along the joint, continuing to melt both the rod and the groove until the entire joint is filled.

Where possible, use a filler rod slightly longer than the joint to be filled. If you run out of filler rod before the weld is complete, taper the end of a new rod and soften it with the welder. Lap the tapered end of the new rod over the end of the rod in the groove and continue.

3 **Cutting off the rod.** Warm the filler rod about 6 mm beyond the end of the joint, then bring the welding nozzle close to the rod and, without fanning, apply a steady stream of hot air to one spot on the rod. Meanwhile, pull gently on the rod; it will thin and then separate.

Continue to lay filler rods into the groove until the surface is slightly higher than the surrounding plastic. When the welded joint is barely warm to the touch, in three to four minutes, cut or file off the ragged ends of the rods.

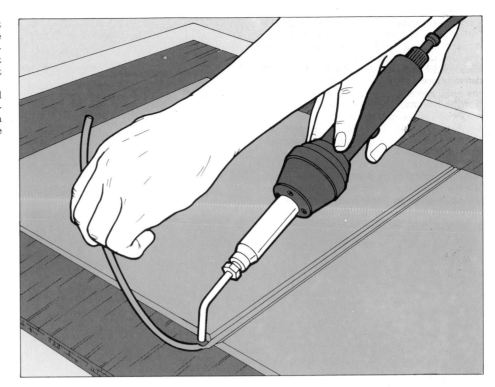

A Strong Angled Joint Made with a Wooden Jig

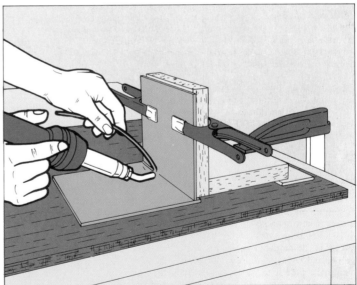

1 **Starting a corner T-weld.** Construct a right-angled jig by nailing together two boards slightly smaller than the plastic sheets being joined. Clamp one sheet upright, against the outside of the jig, aligning the bottom edge with the jig bottom. Place this assembly on top of the other plastic sheet 3 to 6 mm from its edge, forming a T-joint with one short arm. Using the jig as a brace, clamp this assembly to the work surface. Begin welding as in Steps 1 to 3, opposite page and above, laying filler rods into the short arm of the T. Allow the weld to cool for three to four minutes and then remove the cramps.

2 **Completing the T-weld.** Carefully reposition the work so that the jig rests against the outside joint, in the short arm of the T. Prop the jig up with a scrap of plastic to bring it even with the horizontal plastic sheet. Secure the new arrangement to the work surface with cramps. Weld the inside joint as in Step 1. When the weld has had time to cool, remove the cramps and the jig. Using a file or a saw, trim away the excess plastic on the short arm of the T, leaving only the fillet of plastic that forms the outside joint. Also cut or file away the ragged ends of the filler rod, as shown in Step 3, above.

Hole Patches, Big or Little

Plugging a small hole. Fit a round welding nozzle to the torch, and hold the end of a filler rod just outside the edge of the hole—in this case, a hole in a car windscreen-washer reservoir made of polyethylene. Using a fanning motion, soften the filler rod and the plastic surface beneath it. As the two soften, press the filler rod over the hole in the plastic. Cut off the excess filler rod as shown on page 59, Step 3.

For a slightly larger hole, lay the molten rod across the opening in several passes, side by side. Or cover the opening by working in a spiral pattern, from the edge of the hole into the centre.

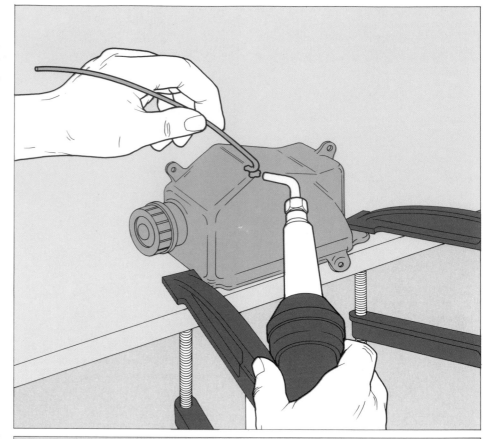

Patching a large hole. Cut a patch from plastic of the same type and thickness as the plastic in the object being repaired, making it at least 6 mm larger than the size of the hole. Lay the patch over the hole and hold it in place temporarily with a stick while you tack-weld the patch to the object *(page 58, Step 1)*. Then exchange the tacking nozzle for a standard round nozzle, and weld filler rod into the joint round the edge of the patch *(page 58, Step 2)*. When you change nozzles, be sure to protect your hand from the hot metal.

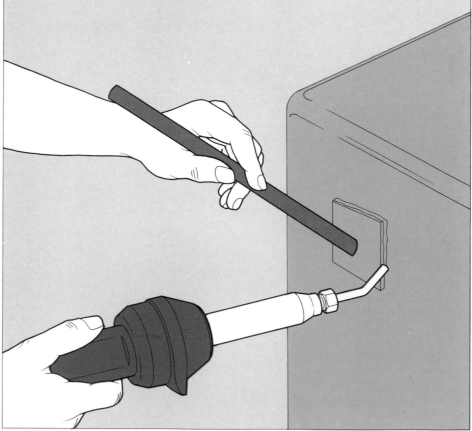

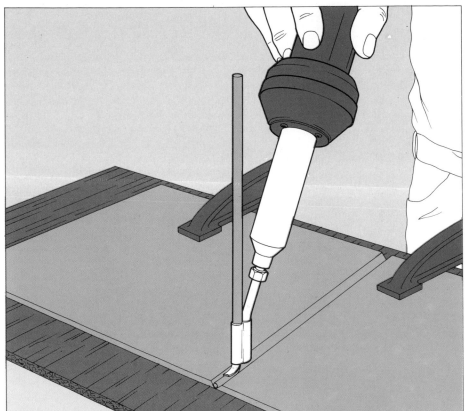

Using a Speed-Welding Tip

1 **Tacking the joint.** Bevel the faces of the plastic so they together form a 60-degree V *(page 58, Step 1)*, then hold or clamp the plastic sheets in position, leaving a 0.5 mm gap between them. Attach a high-speed nozzle to the welder; in this example the nozzle is designed for a round filler rod. Insert the rod into the feeder and hold the heated welding nozzle almost upright, 3 to 6 mm above one end of the joint. When both the tip of the filler strip and the plastic beneath it are melted, use the curved nose of the feeder to push the molten rod into the molten plastic, tacking the end of the joint.

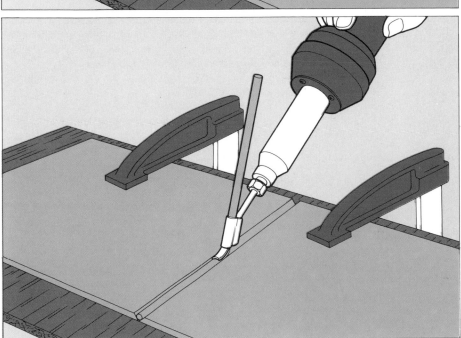

2 **Filling the joint.** Move the welding nozzle, still held upright, along the joint, feeding and pressing more filler on to the plastic until you have fused about 25 mm. Then drop the torch to about a 45-degree angle and pull it slowly along the joint, allowing the filler to feed out of the welding nozzle in a continuous length. As you work, continue to press together the molten filler and the molten plastic beneath it.

3 **Finishing the weld.** At the end of the joint, tilt the handpiece forwards and dig the tip of the nose into the filler rod, severing it. Lift the nozzle back and away from the weld. Immediately remove the leftover filler rod from the hot nozzle, before it has a chance to harden and stick to the tool.

Hems or Seams in Flexible Film

The edges of plastic film and flexible plastic sheets can be heat-welded to form a variety of hems and seams that are useful for making such household items as shower curtains, clothes bags and fitted seat covers. Special heat-sealing tools are available for commercial use, but an ordinary household iron is surprisingly handy for these jobs, efficiently fusing such diverse plastics as polyethylene, polystyrene and polyvinyl chloride. You could, alternatively, use a strip of heated metal previously sprayed with Teflon.

Insulate the work surface from the iron's moderate heat with a sheet of heavy cardboard. To stop the plastic from sticking to the iron or the cardboard, sandwich it between two sheets of non-stick material such as cellophane, for example, or the silicone-coated paper most familiar as the peel-off paper on adhesive-backed plastics. If the iron has a non-stick coating, only the bottom layer of non-stick protective covering will be needed. Generally the iron should be set in the synthetics range and applied to the plastic for just a few seconds, but exact fusion times and temperatures depend on the composition and thickness of the plastic. Experiment with scraps of plastic before attempting an actual project. To guide the iron along a straight seam, butt it against a wooden straightedge; for a curved seam, cut a template from wood or a sheet of heavy cardboard.

Seams may also be fashioned with a Teflon-coated knife attachment on a welding torch *(page 57)*. This tool is well suited to a technique called shrink-wrapping, which uses a special plastic. As the term implies, this material can be wrapped round an object, sealed at the edges, and then shrunk—most commonly with a hot-air gun—to conform exactly to the shape of the enclosed object. Shrinkable plastic can also be sealed with an iron, but the seams will be wider and less attractive.

Another sort of shrinkable plastic comes in tubular form and is most commonly used as a sleeve to gather wires into neat bundles. When heated, this tubular plastic shrinks to half its diameter without losing length. It is available in diameters that shrink to measurements of from less than a millimetre to 25 mm—in any length—and can be shrunk with a hot-air gun, an industrial hot-air blower or even with the heat of a cigarette lighter, because the material is non-inflammable.

A Choice of Three Hems and Two Seams

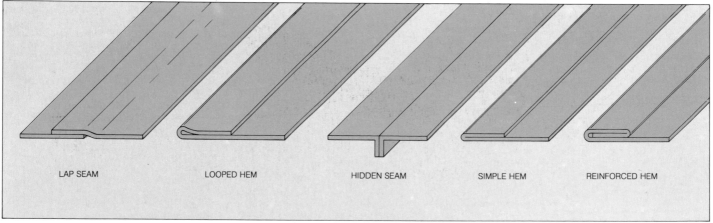

LAP SEAM   LOOPED HEM   HIDDEN SEAM   SIMPLE HEM   REINFORCED HEM

A range of seams and hems. Both the lap seam and the looped hem are made at the edge of the worktable, with the excess plastic overhanging the edge *(opposite page, above)*; the hidden seam and the other two hems are made at the centre of the worktable, with the work supported on both sides *(opposite page, below)*. The lap seam joins two pieces of plastic film by simply overlapping and fusing their ends. The looped hem is folded back on itself and fused in a way that leaves an unsealed channel; a wire or a cord can then be threaded through the channel. The hidden seam is formed by laying two sheets of plastic face to face and sealing their edges; when the sheets are opened out, the seam is on the underside of the work. The simple hem consists of a single fold, sealed on the underside of the work; for the reinforced hem, the fold is doubled.

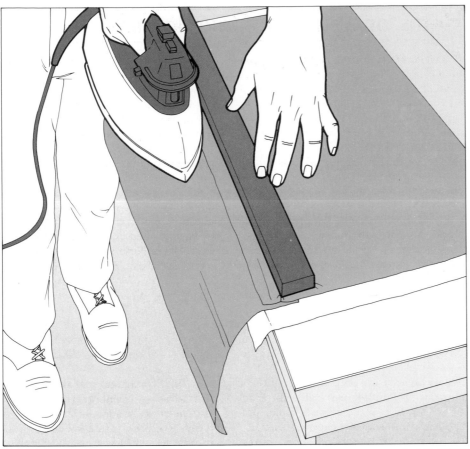

Forming a lap seam or a looped hem. Cover the work surface all the way to its edge with a non-stick protective covering. For a lap seam *(left)*, overlap the two pieces of plastic about 20 mm and position one edge of the seam along the edge of the work surface. Weight the seam along its centre line with a straightedge. (If your iron lacks a non-stick base, place a layer of non-stick covering between the straightedge and the plastic.) Beginning at one end of the seam, lower the iron against the plastic, using the straightedge as a guide, and press down. Lift the iron, move it along the edge and press again. Continue in this way until the seam is fused along its entire length. Then remove the straightedge and seal the other half of the seam.

For a looped hem, fold the plastic back on itself and line up the cut edge of the plastic with the edge of the worktable. Place the straightedge over the hem, covering enough of the fold line to provide a channel of sufficient width for the reinforcing cord. Fuse the area between the straightedge and the edge of the table.

Fusing a hem or a hidden seam. For the seam *(left)*, spread a sheet of non-stick protective covering over the work surface and lay the two sheets of plastic face to face over it, with their edges aligned. If, unlike the iron shown here, your iron does not have a coated soleplate, top the plastic with a second layer of protective covering. Place a straightedge over the layered materials, about 20 mm in from, and parallel to, the edges of the plastic. Press down on the seam with the iron, as described in the caption above, using the straightedge as a guide. When the plastic sheets have cooled, spread them open, turning the seam to the back *(inset)*.

For a simple hem, fold the plastic back on itself once; for a reinforced hem, fold it twice. Sandwich the plastic between two layers of protective covering and place a straightedge along the hem, covering about half its width.

Using the straightedge as a guide for the iron, press down on the hem as for the seam above. Then remove the straightedge and press down the free edge of the hem in the same way.

Shrink-Wrapping with Plastic Film

1 **Shrouding the object with film.** Set up the welding torch and knife attachment, the roll of plastic film, a heatproof pad, and the hot-air gun used in shrinking the film. Turn on the welding torch and allow the knife to heat up for three or four minutes. Unroll enough film to cover the object being wrapped, and slip the object between the two layers of film. Slide the object towards you until it touches the seam at the end of the film.

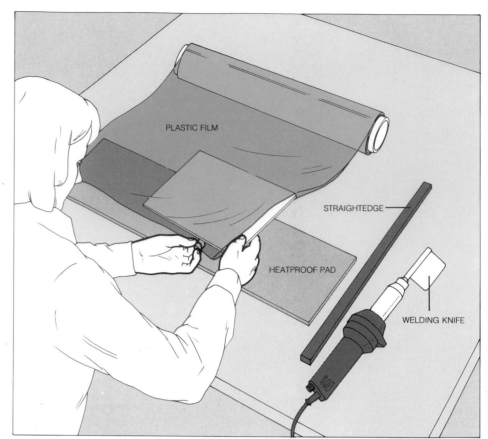

PLASTIC FILM

STRAIGHTEDGE

HEATPROOF PAD

WELDING KNIFE

2 **Cutting and sealing the film.** Place a straightedge on the plastic about 25 mm from the edge of the object, and draw the knife along the straightedge at a steady rate. Trim off excess film with a sharp blade, then turn the plastic-covered object and seal the remaining sides, about 12 mm beyond its edges. Nick this airtight plastic envelope with a blade in some inconspicuous spot to let air escape when the film shrinks.

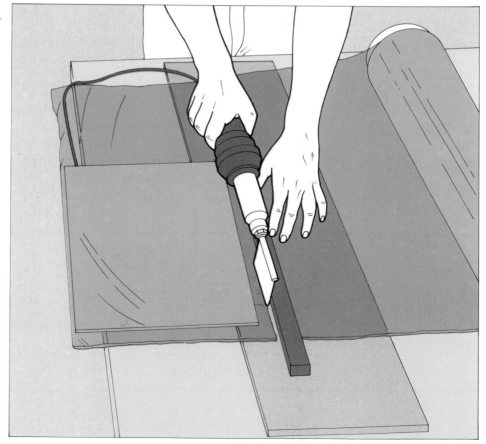

3 Shrinking the film. Rest the plastic-wrapped object on a protective sheet of cardboard and direct a stream of warm air against it with the hot-air gun, moving the gun in a circle and holding it about 75 mm above the surface of the plastic. When the plastic on this side begins to bubble and wrinkle, turn the work over; heat the other side until it bubbles, then pulls taut and smooth. Repeat to smooth the first side.

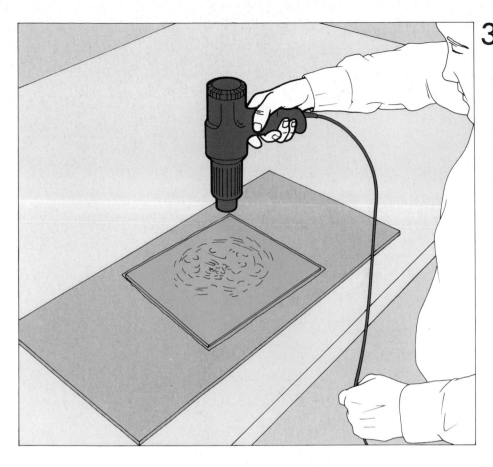

Shrink Tubing Used to Bundle Wires Together

Gathering wires into a bundle. Estimate the diameter of the bundled wires and choose shrink tubing manufactured to shrink to that diameter or slightly smaller. Cut tubing to the desired length; it can cover the entire length of the wires or grasp them only at intervals. Slide the tubing over the wires. Sweep a hot-air gun back and forth over the tubing until it grips the bundle tightly. A similar heat-shrinkable tubing, thick enough to protect bare wires in low-voltage wiring splices, is available at electrical supply shops; it must be heated with the open flame of a match or candle and therefore should not be used to gather already-insulated wires, whose sheathings could be ignited.

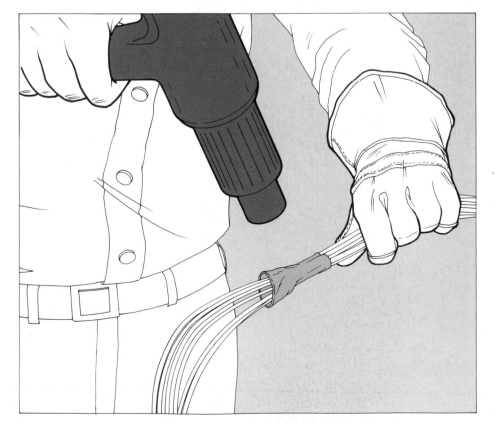

A Primer on Poured Shapes

3

Line-for-line copy. A duplicate doorknob cast from liquid plastic resin has hardened and is ready to be removed from its synthetic-rubber mould. Made in two parts, the mould reproduces the contours of the original doorknob, or master. The mould, too, is a casting: the rubber compound is poured, in two stages, into a box containing the master. Once the compound hardens, the master is removed and the cavity becomes the mould for the new item. In place of the wooden box, built here of scrap timber, the mould frame could be made of Plasticine *(page 76)*.

Although rigid plastics have many useful applications, it is the liquid plastics that truly capitalize on the material's major characteristic—its ability to be moulded into any shape desired. Indeed, most of the plastic objects found in the home are formed by a variety of moulding processes that turn liquefied plastic into everything from contoured tool handles to the appliance housings that neatly follow the functions of the working parts within.

In factories these processes are handled by sophisticated machines that heat and shape the plastic in one continuous operation. Gramophone records, for example, are made by compression moulding: the halves of a 200-tonne press melt the plastic and also form the grooves. Camera parts are formed in an injection-moulding machine, which liquefies plastic pellets and squirts them into a mould under enormous pressure—all in a cycle that may last just 10 seconds. And the familiar squeeze bottle is made by a blow-moulding machine, which forces the liquid plastic against the walls of a mould in a repetitive process that is much like blowing up an endless succession of balloons.

None of these processes can be duplicated in the home workshop, but a surprising number of the objects they create can be produced by simpler means. Liquid resins can be cast in hand-made moulds—of clay, plastic or rubber—that have been shaped around a master, or model; the master may itself be hand-made. Another technique is to layer liquid plastic and fabric over a home-made timber form. Neither approach requires machinery, but they both call for patience, dexterity, and the ability to think in three dimensions. In short, modelling objects in plastic is very like creating a work of art.

Working Safely Amid the Vapours

Casting or laminating plastics releases toxic vapours that require more filtering than a paper dust mask can provide. The answer is a charcoal-cartridge respirator, available from D.I.Y. shops. This piece of equipment consists of a rubber face mask that can be fitted with a replaceable cartridge containing charcoal granules to filter out harmful vapours. On some models the respirator can also be fitted with a fabric filter for dust, which should be used when sanding newly cast fibreglass laminate or when sawing finished laminate.

Some professionals recommend replacement of a cartridge after about 10 hours of use; certainly it should be replaced as soon as any smell or taste is detected. Dust filters should be replaced whenever breathing becomes difficult.

The fit of the respirator is important and should be checked according to the manufacturer's instructions. Clean the mask after use, and store it in a sealed plastic bag.

The standard safety precautions—including no smoking or naked lights and a well ventilated room—must also be observed. Eye protection is essential when sanding fibreglass or laminates.

Rigid Moulds to Shape Liquid Plastic Resins

Many plastic objects found in the home—from doorknobs to kitchen sinks—began as liquid plastic resins that were shaped and hardened in moulds. In factories these moulds are made of hardened steel, to enable them to withstand the wear and tear of mass production. But at home, where the operation is on a much smaller scale, liquid plastics can be shaped in moulds made of such commonplace, easily worked materials as plaster, wood or synthetic rubber. The latter is a moulding compound available at artists' materials shops.

Moulds for forming liquid plastics fall into two categories. Either they are cavities into which liquid epoxy or polyester is poured, or they are contoured forms over which successive layers of plastic are laid, usually in conjunction with a reinforcing material such as, for example, glass fibre. In a variation on this latter moulding technique, shallow reliefs, such as ceiling roses, are cast in surface moulds.

The first step in casting anything in a hollow mould is to examine the object you will duplicate, called the master. Depending on its shape and surface details, you may choose either to make a rigid plaster mould *(opposite page and pages 70–73)* or to use a flexible mould of synthetic rubber *(pages 76–81)*.

If the master has a complex shape, with reverse curves, undercuts and many incised details, a flexible rubber mould will be easier to pull cleanly from its surface. More durable than plaster, a synthetic rubber mould is also preferable if you plan to make many castings of the same shape. Under any other circumstances, however, a rigid plaster mould is better because it is so much cheaper. Make it of moulding plaster, which is finer in texture than wall-patching plaster and therefore gives you a better reproduction. Moulding plaster, commonly called plaster of Paris, is available at most hardware shops.

In some instances, a plaster mould is poured in two parts in a frame built round the master; in other cases, it is made by applying plaster to the surface of a master in multiple sections. This choice, too, depends on the complexity of the master. To determine how many mould parts you will need and where their separations will fall, you must analyse the shape of the master. As a general rule the mould will separate along the widest part of the master. But you must also look for reverse curves or undercuts that would interfere with the removal of the mould unless it subdivides into additional pieces. When you have located the dividing planes between mould parts—called the parting lines—draw them on the master with chalk or a marking pen.

The frame used to contain the liquid plaster for a two-part mould may be a plastic container or a cardboard box. To seal the seams of the box, use masking tape or the pliable rope caulking often used for sealing round windows. If you do not have a ready-made container of the right size, you can build the frame with scrap timber or shape it with potter's clay.

In preparation for pouring, you will also need to plan how to immobilize the master within the frame. If you have made the frame from clay, you can simply add a pedestal of clay for the master or use the technique shown on page 80, Step 1. A wooden, plastic or cardboard frame requires more ingenuity. Depending on the location of the parting lines, you may be able to suspend the master from a wooden crosspiece nailed to the top of the frame. Otherwise, anchor it to the side of the frame with a wooden spacer, fastening the spacer to the master with existing hardware on the master, such as screws or bolts, or with glue; then attach the spacer to the frame with screws.

Whatever anchoring arrangement you use, keep in mind that the anchor also creates the sprue hole for the mould—the hole through which the casting material will be poured.

Before the master is secured in the frame, it must be coated evenly with a mould-release agent. Use either Teflon spray or paraffin, which is applied with an artist's brush. Washing-up liquid can also be used as a release agent, but will leave a less polished surface. Applied in a thin coat with a small brush, the detergent must dry for about five minutes before the plaster comes into contact with it.

Timing is important in mixing and using plaster or a plaster substitute to make a rigid mould. The prepared plaster will remain thin enough to pour for three to five minutes. After that, it will be about as thick as soft cake icing and can be laid over the master by hand for up to another five minutes. Beyond five minutes, it will usually become slightly crumbly, suitable only for patching; in five minutes more, it will become too granular to use at all.

To mix plaster and water, use a flat-bottomed plastic mixing pan and put into it roughly four-fifths as much water as the liquid plaster you need. Sift plaster dust into the pan through your fingers, sprinkling it evenly over the surface of the water until it begins to form small islands of dry plaster on the surface. When these islands take about 10 seconds to become moist, blend the plaster solution with a large metal spoon, stirring it for no more than 30 seconds. It is now ready for pouring.

Although the plaster mould will be hard enough to remove from the master in 15 to 30 minutes, it must dry, or cure, for five to seven days before use. Otherwise, the moisture remaining in the plaster might ruin the casting. When all moisture has evaporated from the plaster, the mould will feel much lighter and its surface powdery rather than clammy. You can accelerate the curing process by putting the mould in a 60°C oven for 12 to 24 hours, depending on its size.

The last step in making the mould is to check the mould's interior surface for flaws. Use paint thinner to remove any paraffin left by the master, then fill or rebuild any pockmarks or chipped edges with cellulose plaster filler. Smooth away any surface roughness with a fine grade of steel wool. If you find that there are cracks or breaks in the cured mould, they can be repaired with PVA adhesive.

Handling Moulding Plaster

☐ Never use stored plaster without first mixing a test batch; if the plaster has absorbed moisture from the air, it will not harden properly.

☐ Control the rate at which liquid plaster thickens by altering water temperature, adding salt or vinegar, or adjusting stirring time. Warm water speeds hardening; small amounts of salt accelerate hardening, and adding vinegar retards it; lengthy stirring makes plaster harden faster.

☐ Cover the work surface with a sheet of polyethylene plastic; plaster does not adhere to this material.

☐ Simplify clean-up by coating the mixing dish and mixing spoon with a light film of paraffin before you start the mixing process.

☐ Rinse your tools in a bucket of water before plaster hardens on them. Let the plaster settle, then dispose of solids and liquids separately. Never pour plaster into your plumbing system.

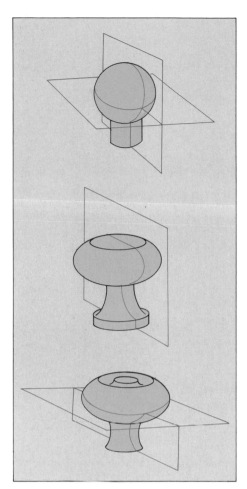

Suiting the Mould Type to the Shape of the Master

Finding the parting line. The sections of a mould meet each other along a flat surface, called the parting line, which is positioned so that each section can be removed from the master without interference. The number as well as the location of the lines is determined by the shape of the master—as illustrated by the three differently shaped doorknobs shown on the left.

With its symmetrical shape, the top doorknob can have either a vertical or a horizontal parting line—a two-part mould would separate cleanly in either direction. The undercut sides of the middle doorknob in the illustration require a mould that separates vertically, to prevent interference from the base of the knob.

The bottom doorknob requires a mould with two parting lines. Because the modelling at the top of the master prevents mould sections from separating vertically, one parting line cuts horizontally through the knob's widest part, sectioning off the top. However, the reverse curve in the base of the knob would prevent the removal of a single mould section there, so a second parting line runs vertically through the knob, from its base to the horizontal parting line.

A Two-Part Mould Made of Poured Plaster

1 **Constructing a fall-away frame.** Using scrap timber, build a box with four sides and a base whose interior length, width, and depth are roughly 30 mm greater than the dimensions of the master—in this example, a decorative coat hook. Connect the sides at the corners with wood screws, then nail the base to the sides with round-head nails or pins.

Draw the parting line on the master with a marking pen. On the inside of the box, draw a cross at the point where the master will be anchored. Extend the horizontal line of the cross mark to use as a guideline in pouring the plaster. Draw a matching cross on the outside of the box.

Seal the inside joints with masking tape, pressing strips of tape into the corners and over the seams between the bottom and the sides *(inset)*. Coat the interior of the box thoroughly with a thin layer of petroleum jelly.

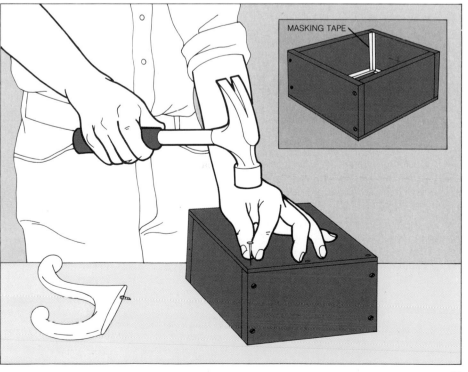

MASKING TAPE

2 **Anchoring the master in the frame.** Cut a wooden spacer to fit the surface on the master to which it will be attached. Fasten the spacer to the master with glue or with any existing hardware—in this example, the coat-hook screw. Then coat both the master and the spacer with a release agent *(page 68)*, taking care not to disturb the parting lines drawn on the master. Position the master in the frame, lining up the horizontal parting line with the cross-mark extension on the box, and drive a screw through the box into the spacer. To avoid marring the coated master, hold the work only by the spacer throughout this operation.

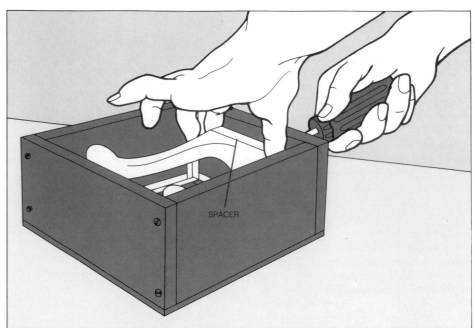

SPACER

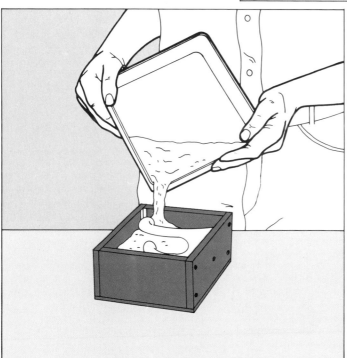

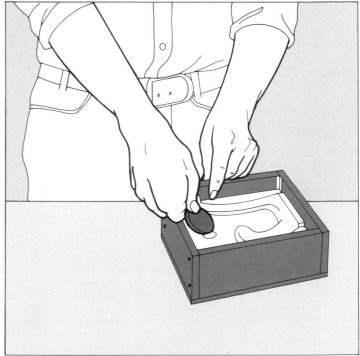

3 **Pouring the first mould section.** In a shallow pan, mix enough plaster to fill the frame to the horizontal parting line, marked on the side of the box. Immediately pour it in a steady stream into the frame until it reaches the parting line. Tap the sides of the box several times with your hand to release any bubbles from the plaster.

4 **Keying the parts.** When the plaster is firm but not yet hard (in about 15 minutes), press the tip of a spoon into its surface to carve out a semicircular indentation—called a key—that will be used in aligning the two parts of the completed mould. Turn the spoon 90 degrees from the direction of the first key and make a second indentation, at right angles to the first.

When the plaster has set (usually in another 15 minutes), coat its surface with a thin layer of release agent. Mix a second batch of plaster and pour it into the frame, completely filling the frame. Again, gently tap the sides of the frame to remove any air bubbles.

5 **Dismantling the frame.** When the second batch of plaster has set, invert the frame and remove all its fasteners, including the screw that holds the spacer to the box. Set aside the parts of the frame and gently separate the two halves of the mould. If the parts stick, insert small wooden wedges between the halves to prise them apart; tap the wedges gently with a mallet. When the parts are separated, remove the master *(inset)*.

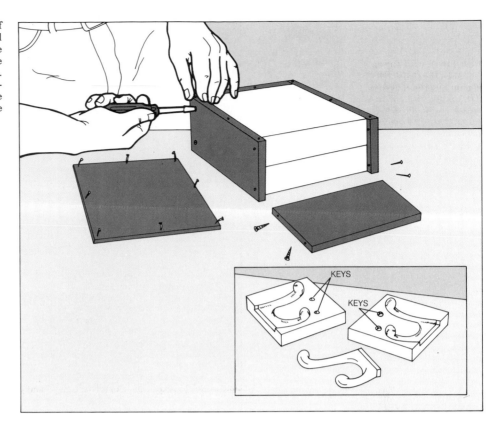

A Three-Piece Mould for Copying a Complex Shape

1 **Creating a clay dam to hold the plaster.** Ring the top of the master with a shallow, saucer-like dam by pressing a 12 mm-wide strip of potter's clay against the horizontal parting line, aligning the top of the strip with the parting line. Cut the strip to size before you apply it, using clay rolled about 3 mm thick. If the dam fails to stay in place, buttress it with vertical strips of clay braced against the work surface.

Pinch two ridges in the top of the dam, on opposite sides of the master, to serve as keys in assembling the finished mould. Then coat the top of the master, above the dam, with a release agent, using the technique described on page 68.

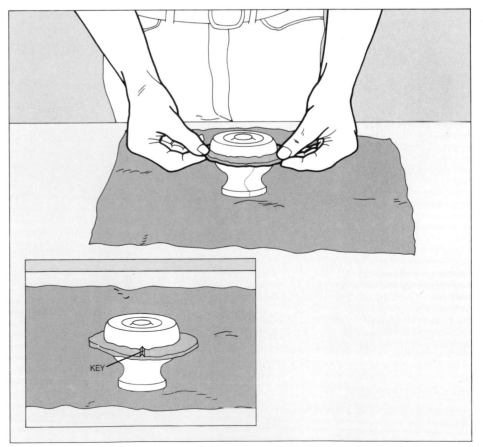

2 **Applying the plaster base coat.** Fill a wide-nozzled squeeze bottle with plaster mixed to a pouring consistency, as described on page 68. Squirt a steady stream of plaster over the top of the master, holding the bottle about 150 mm above the surface and covering the entire area circumscribed by the dam with a thin layer of plaster. When this layer has set, in about 15 minutes, repeat the procedure to build up a double layer of plaster about 3 mm thick.

3 **Applying the top coat.** Mix a batch of plaster and allow it to thicken to moulding consistency, as described on page 68. Using your fingertips as a scoop, daub the plaster over the base coat until the combined thickness of the two coats of plaster equals about 12 mm, just slightly less than the width of the dam.

When the top coat has set, in about 15 minutes, peel off the clay dam and coat the flat edge of the mould with a release agent.

4 **Forming vertical dams.** Make two strips of clay 12 mm wide and 3 mm thick, as in Step 1, page 71. Press them against the master, aligning them with opposite sides of the vertical parting lines; the master will be divided in two sections, one slightly larger than the other. Pinch a ridge at the midpoint of each strip, for keys in assembling the mould. Put a coat of release agent on one section of the master between the two dams.

Apply two coats of plaster to the dammed area as in Steps 2 and 3. When the plaster has set, peel off the two clay dams.

5 **Completing the mould.** Spread a release agent on the flat edges of the second mould piece and on the remaining exposed surface of the master. Build up layers of plaster over this surface, as described in Steps 2 and 3, until the third piece of mould is as thick as the other two pieces.

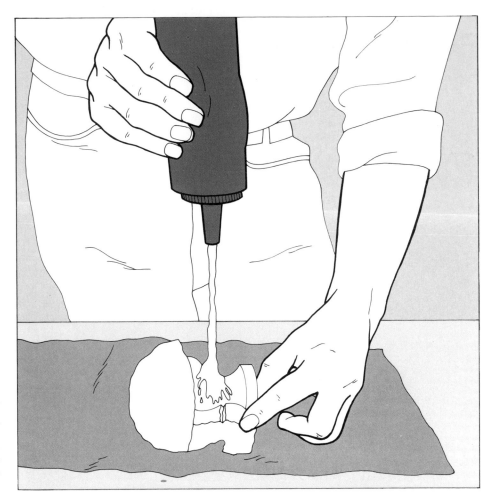

6 **Removing the mould.** When the plaster of the third mould piece has set, separate the mould pieces by driving small wooden wedges into the seams with a rubber mallet. Insert the wedges into the horizontal seam first, placing them at regular intervals round the top mould piece. Gently tap the wedges in succession, driving them in to the same depth to equalize the pressure. When the top piece is free, repeat the procedure to separate the sides, alternately driving wedges into both side seams. When the side pieces separate, remove the master *(inset)*.

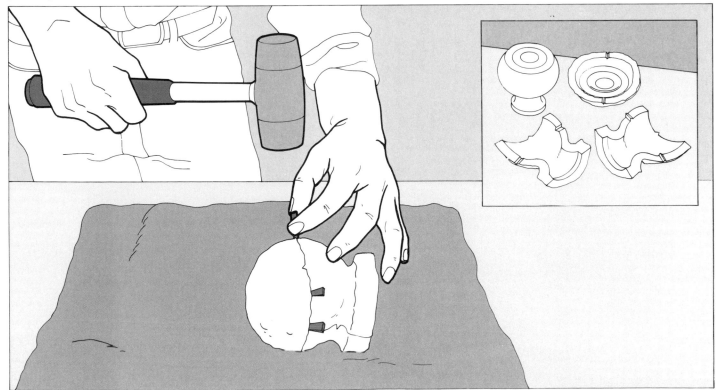

A Wooden Mould for a Fibreglass Shower Base

1 Assembling the sides. To construct the sides of a mould for a shower base, cut four 150 mm-wide pieces of 25 mm-thick chipboard, making two pieces as long as the sides of the planned base and two pieces 50 mm shorter. Cut the ends of the pieces at an angle of 15 degrees, then join the pieces with twinfast chipboard screws to make a four-sided frame, countersinking the screws so that they are below the surface of the wood.

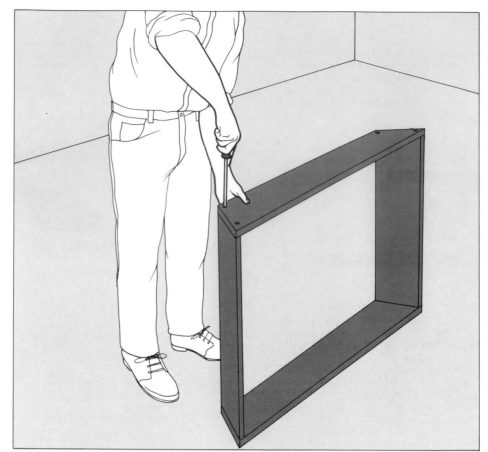

2 Attaching the bottom. Screw four bevelled wooden cleats inside the small end of the frame, positioning them flush with the edge of the frame. Cut a piece of 19 mm chipboard to match the exterior dimensions of the small end of the frame and secure it to the frame by screwing into the cleats. Chamfer the edges of the new piece of chipboard flush with the sloping sides.

Use a putty knife and wood putty to cover the countersunk screw heads and fill any cracks and imperfections in the mould's surface. Sand the entire surface smooth, starting with a medium-grade sandpaper and finishing with a fine grade.

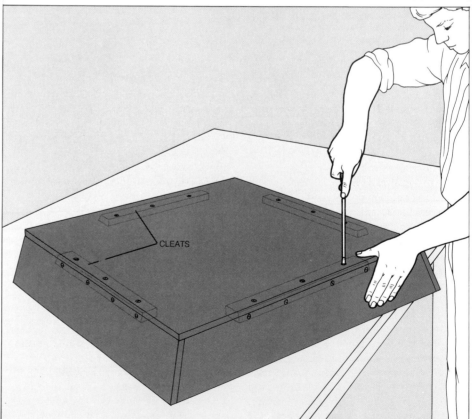

CLEATS

3 Attaching the base. Make a base for the mould with a sheet of 19 mm chipboard 100 mm larger in each dimension than the open end of the frame. Centre the base over the open end of the mould, then screw the base to the frame.

4 Smoothing the inside angles. Use potter's clay to round out the interior angles of the mould. Form the clay into ropes about 12 mm in diameter by rolling it between the palms of your hands and a sheet of polyethylene. Press the clay ropes into the angles between the sides and the base of the mould, simultaneously shaping them to a smooth arc with the bowl of a spoon.

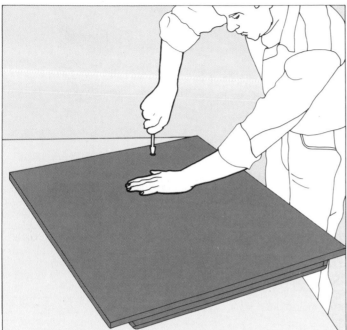
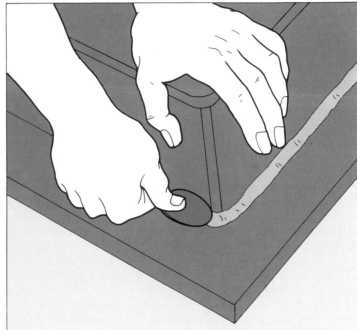

Making Casts of Original Sculpture

Moulds can be used for casting original designs as well as for duplicating existing objects. Once you have mastered the fundamentals of mould-making, it is a short step to the creation of new shapes for any purpose you desire.

Plastic castings are particularly well suited for outdoor use, since the finished products resist the elements. You can fashion fanciful adornments—a fountain, a weather vane, a set of outdoor lanterns, or a jardinière, for example—or replace architectural ornaments such as a finial on a 19th-century gable.

Whatever project you choose, the first step is to sculpt or model a master identical in size and shape to the finished product. The simplest, most popular medium for making a master is potter's clay. Small objects can be formed in solid clay; larger objects, and those with projecting parts, require a reinforcing substructure, called an armature. The armature is built

of wood, galvanized pipe or concrete-reinforcing bar roughly in the shape of the object, then covered with wire mesh for the clay to adhere to. For refining and smoothing the master when it is formed, use the cutting tools, shapers and scrapers sold by artists' materials shops for use with potter's clay.

Plan your mould to suit your master as you would for any object (page 68)—with one exception. If you will be making only one casting from an elaborate master and do not care about preserving the master, you can use plaster to make a disposable mould, called a waste mould, instead of using one of the more expensive flexible moulds (pages 76–81).

In construction, a waste mould is similar to a hollow plaster mould; it is made of plaster layered over a master. But the master is always made of potter's clay, and instead of being separated by clay dams, the sections of the mould are

walled off from each other by rows of metal shims pressed into the master along the parting planes. The shims are crimped at intervals to form keys in the edge of the plaster (page 78, Step 2).

The clay master of a waste mould is considered expendable; pieces of it may stick to the mould during dismantling—especially in undercut areas. These pieces of clay are flushed from the mould surface with a stream of water.

Also expendable are the mould sections themselves. When the casting is complete, the plaster is broken away with a chisel and a mallet. To avoid accidentally damaging the casting, work gently and gradually, with shallow cuts. Or do as professionals do: when you construct the mould, add vegetable dye to the first layer of plaster. Then, when you chip off the mould, a change in the colour of the plaster will warn you that the casting is not far below.

Flexible Moulds to Hold Detail

When you want to cast an object whose contours contain intricate details or an irregular shape, a flexible mould is the best way to ensure faithful reproduction of the original. Similar in principle to a hollow plaster mould (*pages 69–71*) but made with different materials, a flexible mould will bend when removed from the master, so all the eccentric forms and fine details will be preserved intact.

A simple flexible mould for one-time use can be made from Plasticine, an oil-based modelling compound (*page 81*). Moulds that are reusable and suited to more complex shapes are made of synthetic rubber, poured in liquid form round the master—the object being replicated—and allowed to cure, or harden. Of the available types of synthetic rubber—silicone and polyurethane—the less expensive alternative is polyurethane, which is available from D.I.Y. or artists' materials shops.

Polyurethane moulding compound is prepared by combining two components; the resulting chemical reaction makes the mixture set in six hours. Another 10 hours at room temperature is required for the compound to cure completely. Careful weighing of the components with an accurate scale is essential: the smallest error in either component can change the consistency of the mould. If the mould is too soft, it may tear; if too hard, it may crack when pulled from the casting.

The pouring consistency of properly mixed moulding compound resembles that of thick syrup. It remains pourable for only 20 minutes and so should be mixed just before you are ready to pour your mould.

To protect the moulding compound from moisture, which can stop it from curing fully and make the mould susceptible to tearing, use metal, glass or plastic utensils and containers for mixing. Wooden utensils hold moisture, and so do disposable paper containers unless they are plastic-lined. To sculpt an original master instead of making a copy, use Plasticine. When the mould is finished, paint it with paraffin, wrap it in a waterproof covering and store it in a cool, dark, dry place.

The four common types of flexible moulds that are shown here and on the following pages allow you to cast almost any shape. Three are of synthetic rubber; one is of Plasticine.

The simplest of the rubber moulds, ideal for casting flat reliefs, is the one-piece surface mould (*opposite page*). The two-piece shell mould (*pages 78–79*) is the best choice for fragile masters with relatively long vertical axes and varying horizontal diameters. Its external plaster shell lends support to the mould during casting and also reduces cost, since the plaster occupies mould space that would otherwise have to be filled with the more expensive moulding compound. The box mould (*pages 80–81*) is excellent for creating oddly shaped masters, but in making this mould the master is frequently handled. For this reason, the box mould is not recommended for delicate, easily broken masters.

The Plasticine pressed mould (*page 81*), handy for duplicating small, flat reliefs, can be used immediately, without curing. But a Plasticine mould of this kind yields only one casting because, as it is being removed from the casting, the mould must be stretched out of shape.

A One-Piece Surface Mould

1 **Preparing the master.** Rest the master—in this case, a ceiling rose—face up on a wooden block, leaving at least a 25 mm border, then secure the master to this wooden base with a smooth seal of Plasticine. Make an open box around the master by building up four walls of Plasticine at the edge of the wooden base. Make the walls about 12 mm thick and at least 25 mm higher than the highest point of the master. Paint or coat the master, the base and all four interior Plasticine walls with a release agent as described on page 68.

2 **Pouring the mould.** Mix the moulding compound, and pour it into the box until it covers the master by 12 mm at its highest point. Allow the compound to cure for 16 hours at room temperature; then remove the Plasticine walls, invert the mould and lift off the wooden base.

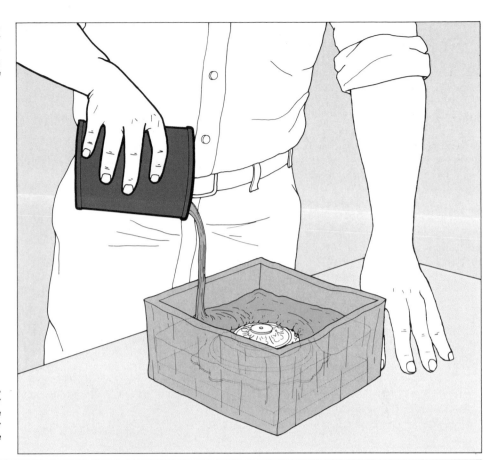

3 **Removing the master.** To loosen the master, grasp the mould on opposite sides and gently bend and twist it (below, left). Then place the mould on a flat surface and remove the master by wedging your fingers between the master and the rim of the mould (below, right).

A Shell Mould in Two Pieces

1 Covering the master with Plasticine. Seal the master—here, a towel-rail bracket—to a wooden base *(page 76, Step 1)*, leaving a border at least 50 mm wide, then cover the entire surface of the master with a blanket of Plasticine 20 mm thick. Construct a solid column of Plasticine at the top of this blanket, about 25 mm high and 25 mm thick, to shape the sprue hole through which the moulding compound will be poured.

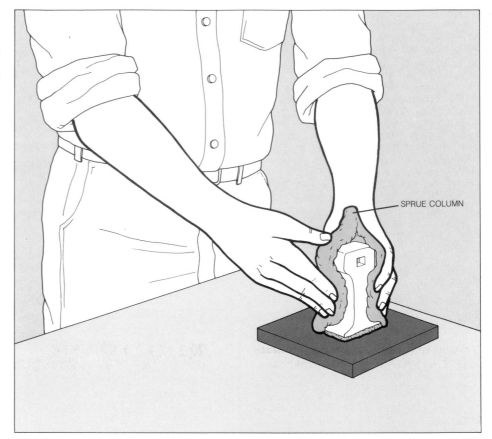

SPRUE COLUMN

2 Implanting shims. Inscribe a vertical parting line down the centre of both sides of the Plasticine blanket, and press metal shims into the Plasticine along the two lines. Cut the shims from disposable aluminium freezer containers (aluminium foil is not stiff enough), making them about 50 mm long and 25 mm wide. Angle a pair of shims on each side to make a key in the plaster shell that will eventually encase them *(inset)*. Overlap the shims so that there is no space between them, but do not carry the line of shims over the top of the sprue column.

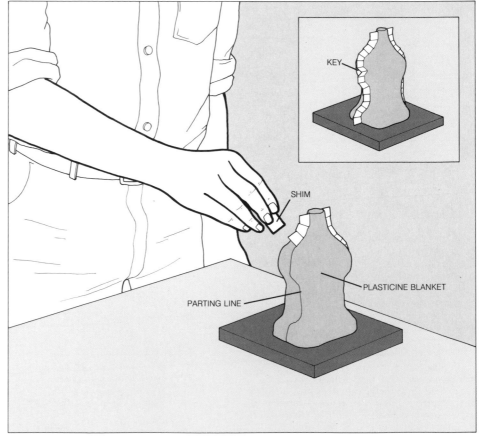

KEY

SHIM

PLASTICINE BLANKET

PARTING LINE

3 **Building the plaster shell.** Cover the Plasticine blanket with a 25 mm-deep layer of moulding plaster *(page 68)*, bringing it level with the top of the shims and the top of the sprue column. Allow the plaster to dry—this usually takes between three and five days.

Mark the outline of the plaster shell on the wooden base, then separate the two halves of the shell along the shim lines. Remove the Plasticine blanket and the shims. Coat the master and the inside of the plaster shell with a release agent *(page 68)*. Then reassemble the shell halves round the master, using the outline on the wooden base as a guide. Fasten the shell halves together with reinforced packaging tape, and seal the shell to the base with a bead of Plasticine.

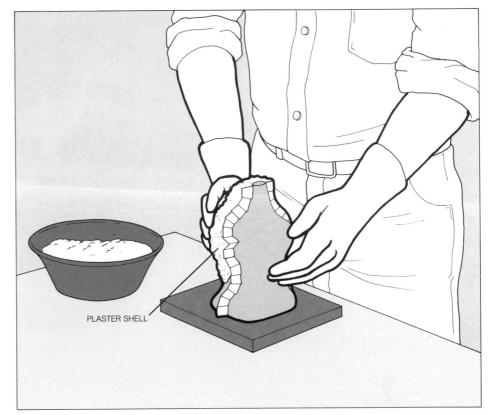

PLASTER SHELL

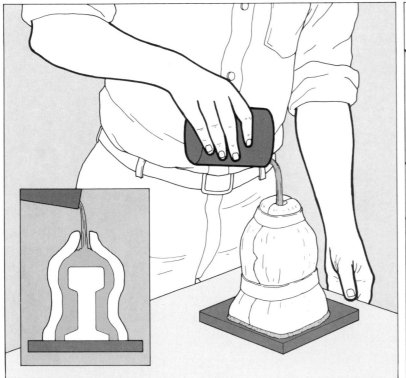

4 **Pouring the mould.** Mix a batch of moulding compound, and pour it into the plaster shell until it rises to the lip of the sprue hole *(inset)*. Allow 16 hours for the mould to cure at room temperature, then separate the halves of the shell and remove it. Lift the mould away from the base.

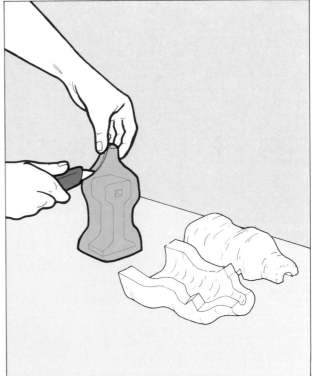

5 **Removing the master.** Use a trimming knife to cut through the finished mould, slicing down one side and half way across the bottom. Gently peel the mould back and remove the master. When casting with the mould, seal the seam with Plasticine to prevent leakage.

A Box Mould for Odd Shapes

1 **Building a Plasticine bed.** Cut a wooden base large enough to leave a 50 mm border round the master—in this case, an ornamental door-knob. Place a layer of Plasticine on the base and rest the master in it so that the parting line, where the two parts of the mould will separate, runs parallel to the base. Build up a bed of Plasticine round the master to the level of the parting line. Then erect a 12 mm-thick Plasticine wall around the bed and base, carrying the wall about 25 mm higher than the highest point on the master. Press the bed against the wall.

Fashion a roll of Plasticine about 12 mm in diameter, and wedge it between the thin end of the master and one wall. Make a similar Plasticine roll about 5 mm in diameter and wedge this between the wall and the widest part of the master. Press the two rolls into half-round shapes that will eventually form two sprue holes—the bigger for pouring liquid resin into, the smaller to allow for the exit of displaced air (*inset*). Then circle the master with a V-groove, carved into the Plasticine bed, to serve as a key for joining the mould parts. Apply a coat of release agent to the exposed master, the Plasticine bed and the inside of the Plasticine walls (*page 68*).

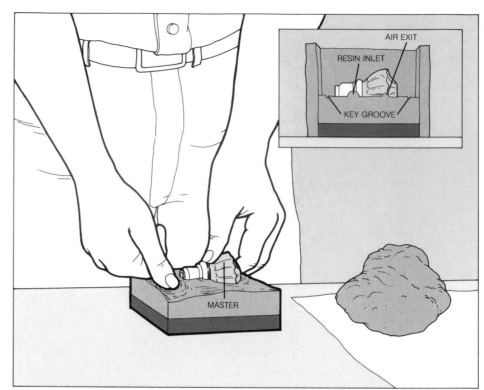

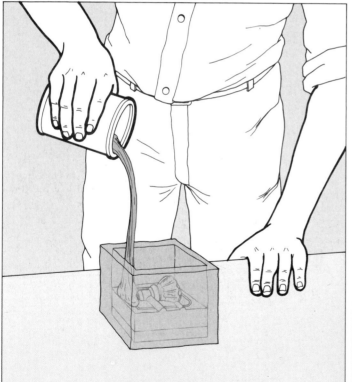

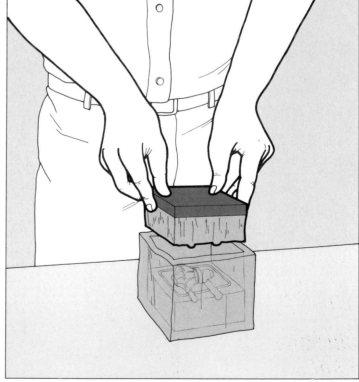

2 **Pouring the first piece.** Mix a batch of moulding compound, and pour it slowly over the master and the Plasticine bed until the level is 12 mm above the highest point of the master. When the moulding compound has set, in about six hours, invert the entire assembly in preparation for pouring the second half of the mould.

3 **Removing the Plasticine bed.** Lift out the wooden base and the Plasticine bed, along with the Plasticine rolls shaping the sprue holes. Repair the wall if necessary. Fit a Plasticine roll into the half-round sprue-hole depressions to complete the sprues. Coat the master, the mould half and the walls with release agent.

4 **Pouring the second piece.** Mix another batch of moulding compound and pour the second half of the mould to a level 12 mm above the highest point of the master. Allow the compound to cure for 16 hours; then remove the Plasticine walls and separate the two halves of the mould. Lift out the rolls of Plasticine forming the sprues.

5 **Removing the master.** Twist the finished mould to loosen the master. Then remove it from the mould. If this mould will not stand on its own during casting, brace it with two squares of wood, cut to size and taped to the sides of the mould.

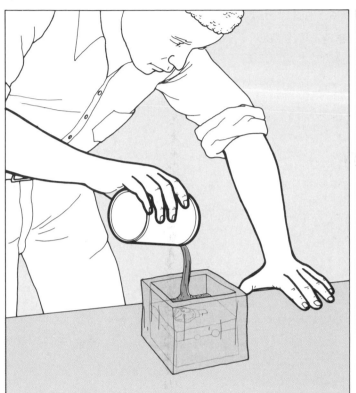

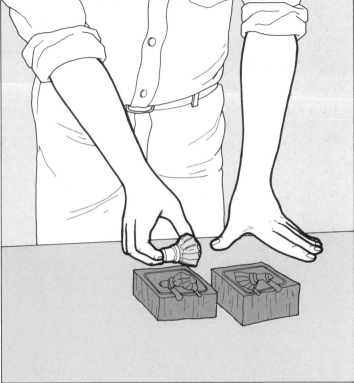

A Simple Pressed Mould for Replacing a Part

Making the mould. Coat the master—in this case, a decorative corner moulding—with a release agent *(page 68)* or a light-grade oil, then push a 25 mm-thick slab of Plasticine on to it, pressing the Plasticine firmly into the detail of the master. Remove the Plasticine carefully and check the impression to be sure that all details have been picked up. Lay the mould flat *(inset)*, and cast a duplicate of the master immediately.

Casting in a Mould: Using Resin in Liquid Form

Although a casting acquires shape and texture from the contours of its mould, its weight, colour and strength are determined by the casting method and the type of materials used. Plastic objects can be cast from three liquid resins: epoxy, polyester or acrylic. Each is combined with a hardener that stiffens, or cures, during casting. But the resins differ in cost, in ease of use and in adaptability to the job.

Acrylics have the greatest optical clarity but cost substantially more than other resins. Epoxy resins normally cure to a translucent amber, although they can also be purchased in clearer formulas. These resins are best used when you want the casting to look like a filler material such as stone dust, powdered wood or powdered metal. Because of their greater adhesive properties, epoxies can hold more filler than other resins can; they can also be combined with a diluent, or thinner, that increases this capacity. Several formulations of epoxy resins and hardeners are available; to be sure of getting the best combination, discuss your particular needs with the plastics supplier.

Polyester resins are the least expensive, most versatile liquid plastics. Almost as clear as the acrylics, these resins allow the greatest margin of error in mixing. However, pure polyester resins shrink more than other resins as they cure.

When size is critical, you can compensate for shrinkage in either of two ways. For solid castings, you can introduce more resin into the mould by extending the sprue with a collar of clay; as the resin in the mould shrinks, more resin seeps in from the reservoir in the sprue. With hollow castings, in which the resin is painted on to mould sections before assembly, shrinkage along the seams is controlled by the use of a resin containing polyester putty, a dimensionally stable filler that clings to the mould edges.

The casting process begins with mould preparation. A plaster mould must be sealed with shellac to make it smooth and non-absorbent. Flexible moulds need no finishing but, like plaster moulds, they must be coated with a mould release or a parting agent, so that the cured casting will slip easily from the mould. The most effective parting agents to use are polyvinyl alcohol or grease.

To stabilize an irregularly shaped mould during the curing process, add wads of clay or place the mould in sand. Once the cured casting is removed from the mould, it can be finished like any plastic. You can cut off any unwanted projections with a dovetail saw or a hacksaw, and file and sand any rough spots that are left on the casting, then polish as desired.

During the casting process, work in a well-ventilated area and always use a charcoal-cartridge respirator. Wear rubber gloves and an old shirt with long sleeves. If you get any resin on your skin, use acetone to remove it, then wash with soap and water and apply a skin lotion.

Everything you will need for casting plastic resins is available through plastics suppliers or D.I.Y. shops.

Techniques for Mixing and Pouring Liquid Resins

The appearance and performance of a casting made with liquid plastic resins depend on careful measuring and mixing. Mix the ingredients together thoroughly, but take care that you do not introduce moisture or air bubbles.

Ingredients for epoxy and acrylic resins should be measured by weight with an accurate scale. Mix hardener for polyester resins by the drop. The proportion of resin to hardener depends on the characteristics you want. In general, the higher the proportion of hardener to resin, the shorter the curing time; but humidity, temperature and the thickness of the casting also affect how fast or slowly the resin cures. To adjust the proportions, mix several test batches under the actual conditions of use, then pick the one that produces the best combination of curing time and physical properties for your purpose. Keep in mind that the faster the curing, the more brittle the casting will be—but a casting that cures too slowly may remain rubbery.

To avoid air bubbles in the finished resin, handle the liquid ingredients with care. When preparing to mix them, pour them slowly down the side of the mixing container or mould. Mix gently but thoroughly; if bubbles form, paddle them to the surface. If you are using the mixing attachment of a power drill to combine the ingredients, start or stop the drill with the attachment completely immersed in the resin and then run the drill slowly to avoid bubbles.

Make sure that all mixing containers are clean and dry and do not have a wax lining, which could contaminate the resin with wax or moisture. For stirring, use a narrow kitchen spatula made of metal, nylon or polypropylene.

The following guidelines give the correct sequence for mixing most resins, hardeners, pigments and fillers:

☐ RESINS AND HARDENERS. Weigh the resin and hardener separately. Always be sure to pour the hardener into the resin. For polyester resin, add the hardener to the resin one drop at a time.

☐ RESIN AND PUTTY. Pour polyester resin into the polyester putty, then add the cream hardener supplied with the polyester putty. Measure the hardener by squeezing specified lengths from the tube on to your stirrer.

☐ ADDING PIGMENTS. To colour acrylic and epoxy resins, add pigments a little at a time to both resin and hardener until each is the desired colour, then pour the hardener into the resin. To colour a polyester resin, add the pigment to the resin only, then add hardener. To colour a polyester resin-and-putty mixture, first combine the putty and resin, then add the pigment, and finally add the cream hardener to the mixture.

☐ ADDING FILLER MATERIAL. Add powdered wood, stone dust, or powdered metal to polyester resins and putty resins following the same sequences used for adding pigments. With epoxies, thin the resin first with a diluent, add hardener, then add filler.

Pouring a Solid Casting in a Flexible Mould

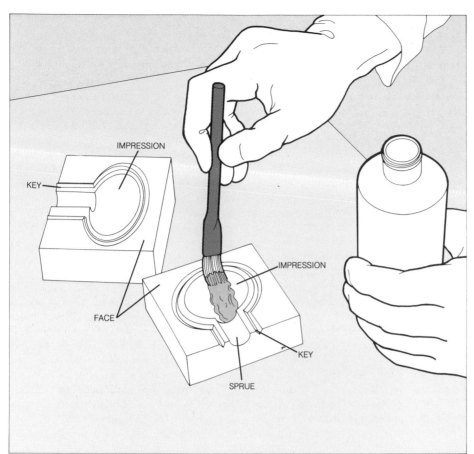

1 **Applying the mould release.** Using a small brush, cover the entire inside of both halves of the synthetic-rubber mould—in this case, for an oval doorknob—with a coating of polyvinyl-alcohol mould release, including the face and key as well as the mould impression and sprue. When the alcohol in the mould release has dried, leaving only a slick surface, apply a second coating. If there are undercut areas of the mould that are difficult to reach with a brush, pour a small amount of the mould release directly into the mould and swish it round; then pour out the excess. When the second coat of mould release has dried, join the two parts of the mould by fitting the keys together.

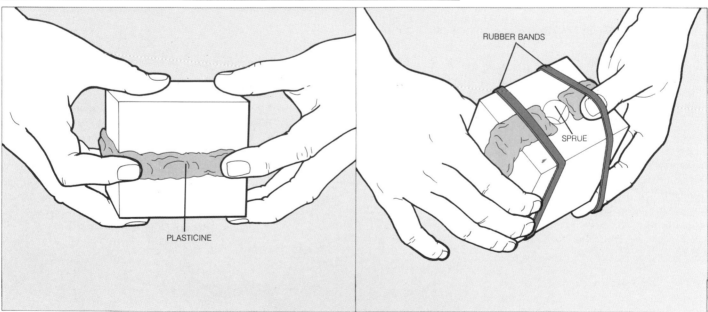

2 **Sealing the mould.** With the two halves of the mould held securely together, press a strand of Plasticine modelling clay, about 20 mm in diameter, along the seam line *(above, left)*, sealing off all but the sprue hole through which the resin will be poured. For convenience, work with small lengths of clay, overlapping their ends by about 25 mm. Then snap wide, flat rubber bands around the two halves of the mould at intervals of about 25 mm *(above, right)*. Do not let the rubber bands cover the sprue hole, and do not make them so tight that they warp the mould or press it out of alignment. Snap a second set of rubber bands over the mould, at right angles to the first.

Mix resin, hardener, pigments and fillers according to the manufacturer's instructions and the guidelines opposite. Be sure, at this point, to put on a charcoal-cartridge respirator.

3 **Filling the mould with resin mixture.** Hold the mould, slightly tilted, sprue hole up, and pour the resin mixture slowly into the sprue. Let the resin slide gently down into the mould, following the contours of the casting impression; this will reduce the number of air bubbles that form.

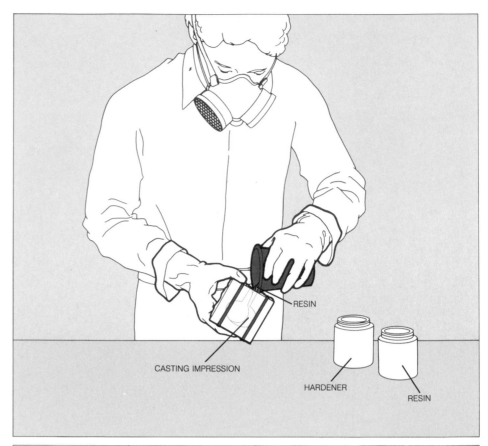

RESIN

CASTING IMPRESSION

HARDENER

RESIN

4 **Removing air bubbles.** Hold the filled mould at an angle, sprue up, and tap it lightly several times against the work surface. Turn the mould one quarter revolution and, with the sprue still angled up, tap it against the surface again. Continue turning and tapping the mould until you return to the original position. Set the mould aside, sprue up, and allow the casting to cure.

Use the resin left in your mixing cup to determine when the casting has cured. When the surface of the resin in the cup is no longer tacky to the touch, press your finger firmly against it. The casting has cured when your finger no longer leaves an impression. Remove the casting from the mould by taking the rubber bands and Plasticine off and pulling the two halves of the rubber mould apart. One half will still be clutching the casting. Simply peel the mould from the casting. Remove any defects and finish the casting as described on page 87.

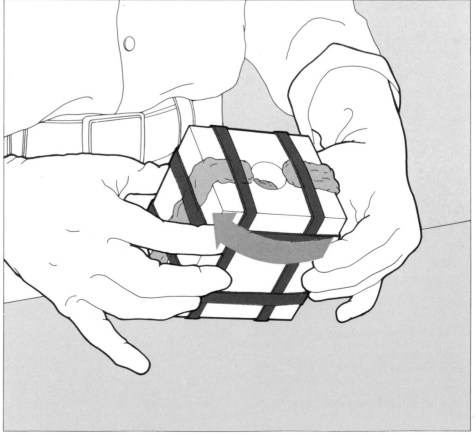

Making a Hollow Casting in a Rigid Mould

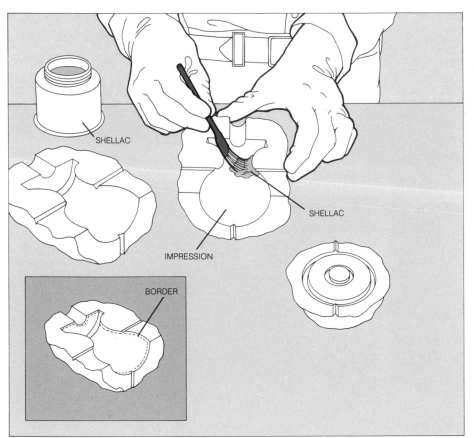

SHELLAC

IMPRESSION

SHELLAC

BORDER

1 **Preparing the mould interior.** To cast the hollow knob used in this example, coat the inside face of each part of the plaster mould with shellac, using a small brush with nylon or natural bristles. Handle the mould pieces gently to prevent chipping. When the shellac is dry, in six to eight hours, spread mould release over the impression, as in Step 1, page 83, but stop 3 mm short of the edge of the impression *(inset)*. The resulting border will allow the resin to grip the edges of the mould pieces while curing, and thus reduce shrinkage along the seams.

Mix a casting compound consisting of three parts polyester putty to one part polyester resin; use a cream hardener and add any pigments desired. Be sure to wear a charcoal-cartridge respirator during the mixing process.

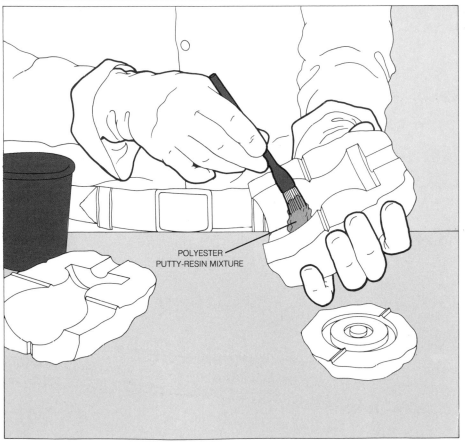

POLYESTER
PUTTY-RESIN MIXTURE

2 **Coating the mould with resin.** Use a small brush to spread the polyester putty-resin mixture evenly into the impression on each piece of the mould. Cover the impressions completely, including the gripping border, with a coating about 1 mm thick. When this coat has partially cured to a gelatinous consistency (usually after about 10 minutes) mix another batch of putty and resin, then brush on another coat. Mix and add a third layer when the second has partially cured, building up a combined thickness of about 6 mm.

3 **Assembling the resin-coated mould.** Fit the parts of the mould together in proper alignment and secure them temporarily with rubber bands or light-gauge wire. Then drill holes sideways through the seams of the mould with a high-speed twist drill bit, spacing the holes about 100 mm apart. Drive wood screws—use a size slightly larger in diameter than the drill bit—through the holes and then take off the temporary fasteners.

If the mould seams are not thick enough to support screw holes, fasten the mould together with light-gauge wire, twisting the ends of the wire to tighten it against the mould (inset).

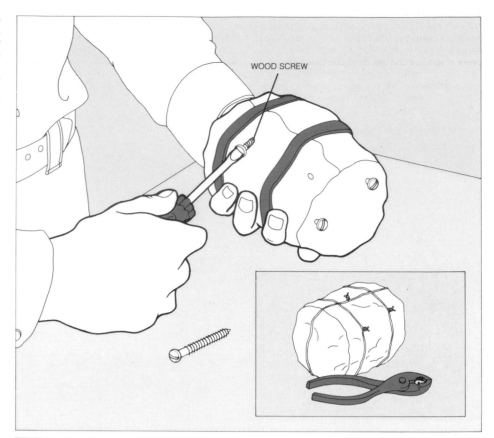

WOOD SCREW

4 **Adding a bonding coat of resin.** Mix a further batch of resin and pour it into the mould through the sprue hole. Swirl it round so that it coats the inside of the casting and fills any hairline cracks at the seam lines; pour out the excess. When the first bonding coat has hardened, add further coats if desired, increasing the thickness of the casting by about 1 mm each time.

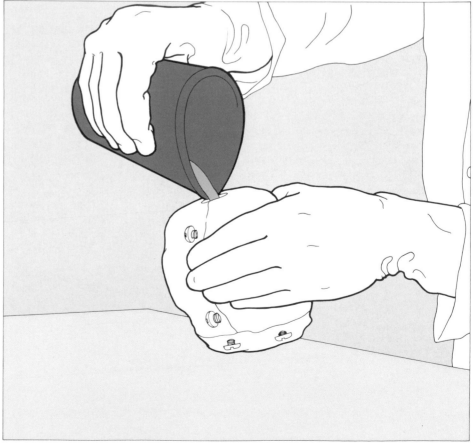

5 **Reinforcing the seams.** While one of the internal bonding coats is still gelatinous, push a piece of resin-impregnated glass fibre mat through the sprue hole *(below, left)*. Spread the glass fibre and press it against the inside of the casting with a thin rod or with your finger, if possible *(below, right)*. If the casting you are working with is a large one, insert additional pieces of glass fibre for extra reinforcement. Lap the glass fibre over the seams of the separate pieces of the mould, thoroughly bonding them together.

When the casting has hardened, remove the screws or the wires holding the mould together. Gently separate the pieces of the mould, pulling them away from the casting one by one. If the mould does not separate easily, hammer lightly on wooden wedges to gently prise the pieces apart along the seams.

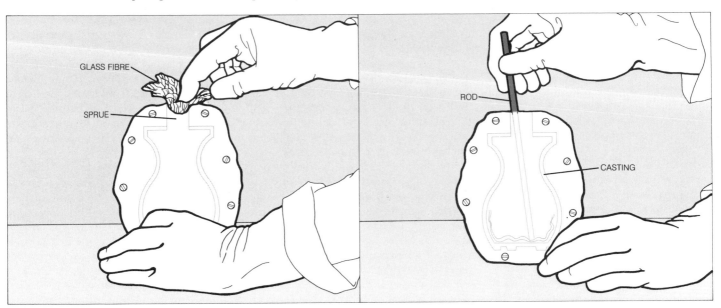

Refining the Details of the Finished Casting

Removing surface imperfections. Use the rasp-like faces and edges of small woodworking tools called rifflers *(inset)* to carve or shave away blemishes acquired during the curing process or while the casting was being removed from the mould. If a defect is extensive, restore it with a resin patch *(page 105)*, and use rifflers to sculpt detail into the patch. A small chisel or trimming knife can also be used for this purpose.

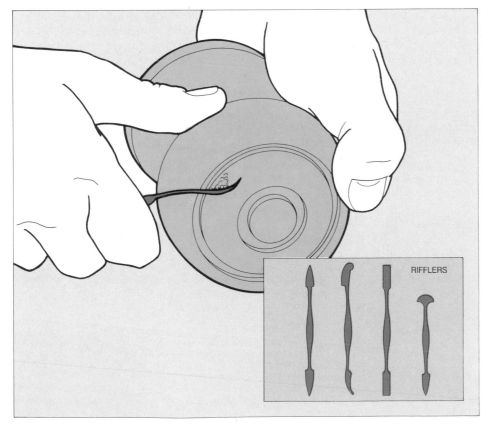

Glass Fibres Reinforced with Plastic Resin

Few building materials can match the versatility and utility of home-mixed glass-fibre-reinforced plastic, commonly called fibreglass. Strong, lightweight and completely weatherproof, it can be moulded into free-form shapes, such as basins or furniture, or laminated to make decorative wall panels, sills or roofing. Formed of woven or felted glass fabric embedded in a plastic resin, the material combines the best attributes of both. The strength of glass fibres in the fabric reinforces the weak, brittle plastic; the plastic makes the material rigid and gives it a smooth, impermeable surface.

For an even stronger material, the proportion of glass to resin is increased within a range of 30 to 70 per cent of the total weight. The glass content is determined by the density and arrangement of the glass filaments in the fabric and by the amount of resin used to laminate it.

The glass fibre fabrics that are used in laminating *(below)* are all made up of rovings—bunched strands of glass filaments. The rovings are pressed or woven into fabrics of varying densities; density is measured in terms of the weight, in grams per square metre of fabric. The fabric weight, as well as the forming method to be used, determine the quantity of resin that will be needed. Generally, a chopped-strand mat takes two and a half times its weight in resin; the ratio of resin to fabric for a woven scrim is 2 to 1.

Fabric choice depends on the amount of reinforcement needed and on the type of resin that is to be used. The bonding agents in glass fibre fabrics are designed to bond with different resins; in purchasing the fabric, be sure that you specify the resin you have selected. Because woven fabrics, which are stronger, will not bond as well with each other as they will with mat fabrics, it is best to alternate layers in order to ensure even strength throughout the laminate. And to produce a smooth surface, a fine glass fibre mat is often used for the layer just beneath the final coat.

Although many resins are suitable for making fibreglass, polyester is both the simplest to use and the most economical, and it provides excellent strength and moisture resistance. When it is laminated, polyester's normal shrinkage of 10 to 15 per cent during curing is reduced to 2 per cent or less, and this slight shrinkage is often an advantage: in moulded laminations, it allows the finished object to slip easily from the mould. Polyester resin is usually available as a two-component system, with resin in one container and the hardener—often known as the catalyst—in another. Be sure to follow the manufacturer's mixing instructions exactly, combining the components carefully to avoid mixing in air bubbles, which weaken the cured resin. For detailed information on measuring and mixing resins, see page 82.

Usually the resin includes an accelerator, also called a promoter, which speeds the curing time, but sometimes this component must be added separately. If you are adding an accelerator, be absolutely sure that you mix it into the resin before introducing the catalyst or hardener. The catalyst must be handled with great care at all times: it is a corrosive substance and can explode on impact.

A special resin called the gel coat is always used as the outermost layer in fibreglass lamination. This unreinforced resin provides a smooth, glossy, protective layer between the glass fibre and outside moisture. It is applied as the first layer if the fibreglass is being built up in a mould, but as the final layer on a flat lamination. By using a tinted gel coat, either pre-mixed or mixed on the job with up to 10 per cent of a suitable polyester tinting paste, you can impart the surface colour of your choice to the fibreglass.

Gel coats come in several formulations. An air-curing type is easiest to handle; it is viscous and less likely to run or, when dry, to crack. Ideally, it should be applied with a

A Glossary of Glass Fabrics for Laminating

Chopped-strand mat. The most common fibreglass reinforcement is a felt-like fabric of short, randomly arranged glass strands held together by a binding agent. Standard 450 g/m² mat is well suited for making reinforced fibreglass roofing sheets and wall panels. Glass fibre mat is stiff and difficult to form until the binding agent dissolves in the resin.

Woven roving. Excellent for reinforcing walls, joints and corners, woven roving provides great strength. Because the coarse weave tends to cause air bubbles to form in the resin between layers, woven roving is usually alternated with layers of mat to prevent delamination. The coarse weave also makes woven roving unsuitable as a surface layer, since the weave shows through the surface resin. Heavier grades of woven roving are too stiff to be used with ease in home workshops.

brush in a single coat not less than 0.5 mm thick. If it is the first layer, it should be thoroughly cured before the laminating resin is applied; otherwise, the solvent in the laminating resin could react with the gel coat and damage its finish. The gel coat should also be compatible with the laminating resin you are using.

When you are laminating fibreglass with a mould or form from which it will later be removed, you will need a release agent to stop the fibreglass from sticking. For simple moulds, you can coat the mould surface with lacquer spray; for large or complex moulds, a two-stage parting compound of hard wax and polyvinyl alcohol is generally used. Apply the wax first and let it dry completely; then, when the wax has dried, apply the alcohol, using a sponge to lay on a thin, even coat. Protect the surface of the mould from dust while the parting compound is drying.

Reduce all the glass fibre fabric to the proper size before mixing the resin. This can be done with scissors or a trimming knife, or the fabric can be torn by pulling it over the edge of a handsaw. If the fabric edges are to be lapped, comb or fray the edges of the glass strands on the overlapping edges so that they will intermingle within the resin and make a joint without a visible seam.

To impregnate the glass fibre with resin, use a paint roller or a brush, stippling the brush over the fabric so as not to dislocate the glass strands with the sticky, resin-coated bristles. Never apply more than the amount of resin recommended by the manufacturer to the fabric; the heat generated by the resin as it cures can adversely affect the laminate if it is applied in quantities too great.

Some polyester resins cure completely only in the absence of air; left exposed, they remain tacky indefinitely. This can be an advantage in multilayer lamination over a large area, where new coats are usually applied before the previous coat cures—a forming process called wet-on-wet. The work can be interrupted for several hours without harming the laminate. When using such resins, however, the final coat must be sealed with a gel coat or covered with an airtight layer of polyethylene film until the resin cures, after which the film can be peeled off. Alternatively, the final coat of resin can be painted with acetone, which dissolves the uncured resin but leaves a rough surface.

Because working with resin is messy, use disposable utensils for measuring and mixing it whenever possible. Keep tools soaking in solvent so that you will be able to clean them when the job is completed, before the resin hardens. A supply of clean rags is essential for removing spilled resin, and the floor beneath the work should be covered with newspapers to catch drips, which are difficult to remove once they have had time to harden.

In addition, the laminating process also requires you to use several specialized tools. One of these tools is a metal disc roller for consolidating the resin and glass and at the same time pushing out any air bubbles that form between layers. These rollers come in several forms, with washer or paddle-shaped blades, and in sizes ranging from 6 to 300 mm wide. For use on contoured surfaces there is a flexible roller, with a head resembling a length of coiled spring. To trim and finish the completed lamination, you will need a metal-cutting saw, a forming tool, and a supply of wet and dry sandpaper from 240 to 600 grit.

Most of the components that are used in laminating fibreglass are irritants. Always wear a respirator and goggles when you are cutting or sanding fibreglass to protect yourself from the fine glass fibres that are released into the air, and be sure to protect your skin with gloves when you are handling the material. Both the resin and its hardener are caustic, inflammable and toxic. Work with them in a well-ventilated place, away from flame, and keep them away from skin and eyes.

Because of the large quantities of resin often involved, laminating is best done outdoors, where the fumes are less dangerous. But do not work outdoors when temperatures are below 12°C, or the resin will cure too slowly. Also, avoid direct sunlight and hot or cold draughts, as these can adversely affect the curing process.

Glass scrim twill. Finer and more flexible than standard woven roving, scrim twill is a good choice for covering irregular shapes and compound curves. Standard scrim twill offers excellent resistance to stress, and is often alternated with mat for high-strength laminates.

Surface mat. A felt-like material, finer than ordinary mat, surface mat comes in a range of different weights. It is used as a smooth final layer to conceal the texture of coarse fabrics.

Weatherproofing a Table for Use Outdoors

1 Cutting fabric to fit. Cut standard grade scrim twill to cover the top and edge of the table, adding 50 mm along each edge to lap to the underside. If the tabletop is too large to cover with one piece, cut two pieces with a 12 mm overlap; then fray the overlap until the strands of fabric can be intermingled and pressed flat. Tack the fabric to the table edge near each corner, then cut away a square of fabric at each corner so that the fabric will fold flat at the corners; again allow for about a 12 mm overlap round each corner of the table, and fray the overlap so that the strands can be pulled round the corner.

Remove the tacks and carefully lift the fabric from the table. Using an orbital or belt sander with coarse abrasive paper, sand the tabletop and edges to remove all paint, dirt and grease; round all the edges. Countersink any screw heads or bolt heads, and fill all holes with wood putty.

2 Priming the surface with resin. Using a paint brush, apply a thin primer coat of resin to the top and edges of the table and to 50 mm of the underside. Mix the resin according to the manufacturer's instructions, then thin it to the consistency of paint by adding a bit of acetone.

Allow the primer coat to harden partially (about 45 minutes) while you clean tools with acetone. When the primer coat starts to harden, mix another batch of resin but do not thin it. Then apply a second coat over the primer coat. A paint roller can be used instead of a brush, but it may produce bubbles in the resin.

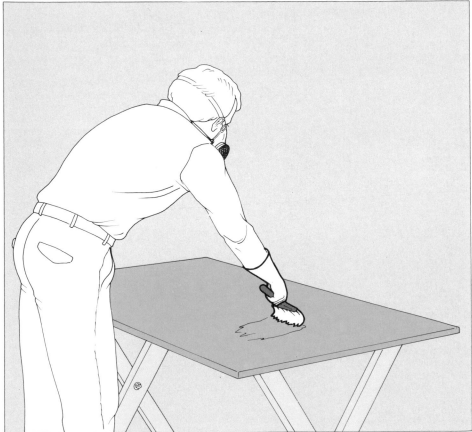

3 **Laying the glass fibre fabric.** Get a helper to hold one end of the pre-cut glass fibre fabric away from the resin-coated table while you align the other end with one corner of the table. Then lower the fabric into the resin, lapping it over the edges and underside and intermingling the frayed strands at the corners. Avoid wrinkles; if the fabric must be moved, lift it and realign it. When the fabric is in place, stipple it with a resin-filled soft-bristled brush until it is completely flat.

For a large table, repeat this procedure, covering the other half of the table with glass fibre. Overlap the frayed edges of the two pieces of fabric by 12 mm, flattening the frayed strands so that the seam line will be invisible.

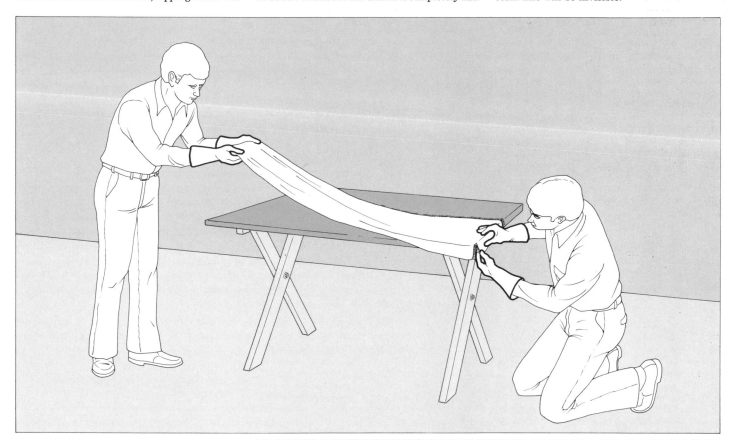

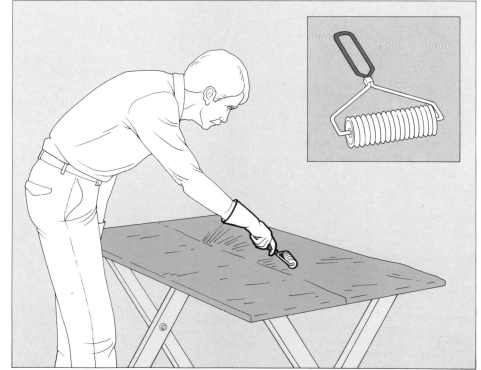

4 **Rolling down the fabric.** Force the fabric into the resin with a disc roller *(inset)* or a brush, working from the centre of the table out to the edges. Roll out any air bubbles, then check to make sure that all the fabric is saturated with resin. Let the resin cure for two hours; meanwhile, clean the tools.

Cover the laminate with an air-drying gel coat, adding tinting paste *(page 88)* if you require colour in the final surface. Use a soft-bristled paintbrush to lay on the gel in an even coat, about 1 mm thick.

Moulding a Base to Use in a Shower Cubicle

1 **Making a pattern.** If the mould is not smooth or if it is porous, coat it with a solution of shellac or cellulose acetate. Then cut from brown wrapping paper a pattern large enough to cover the mould. Shape this paper pattern to the mould, cutting away the excess paper at the corners but allowing for an overlap of 12 mm wherever possible.

Use the paper pattern to cut four pieces of glass fibre fabric: two of standard grade mat, one of standard grade twill, and one of thin surface mat. Cut the fabric with sharp scissors. Fray the overlapping edges as in Step 1, page 90.

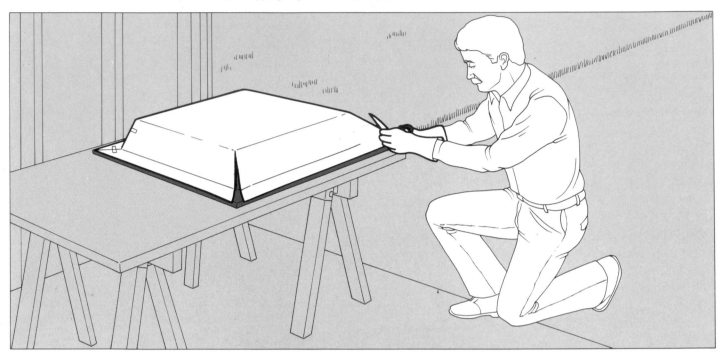

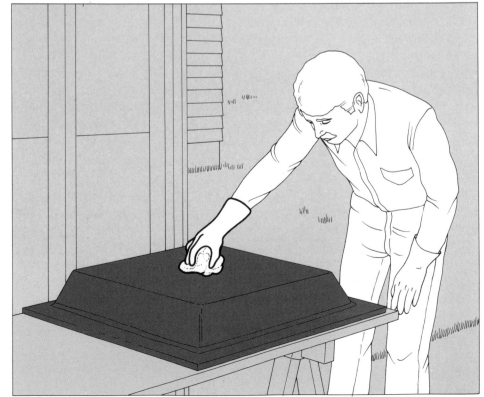

2 **Applying the parting agent.** Use a rag to apply a coat of paste wax on the surface of the laminating mould; polish the wax by rubbing in a circular motion with a lint-free cloth. Apply and polish two more coats of wax. Then use a square-edged plastic sponge to apply a thin, even coat of polyvinyl alcohol over the entire mould. Work with smooth strokes, always in the same direction, and overlap successive strokes so as to avoid the possibility of gaps and streaking.

3 **Laying on the laminate.** Mix a batch of air-drying gel coat sufficient to cover the entire mould. Use a soft-bristled paintbrush to apply the gel coat to the mould and to a small piece of scrap polyethylene. When the gel coat on the plastic scrap is tacky (usually in about 30 minutes), mix a batch of laminating resin to cover the entire mould.

Using a paint roller with a 12 mm nap, coat the mould with laminating resin. Then lay the pre-cut glass fibre surface mat over the mould, using a helper to align it *(page 91, Step 3)*. Work the fabric into the resin with a soft-bristled brush and remove air bubbles with a disc roller *(page 91)*, taking special care to flatten the loose strands at the corners. Before the resin cures, apply successive coats of resin and fabric in the same manner, starting with a layer of mat, then a layer of twill, and finally a second layer of the mat. Compress each layer and roll out air bubbles before adding the next coat of resin.

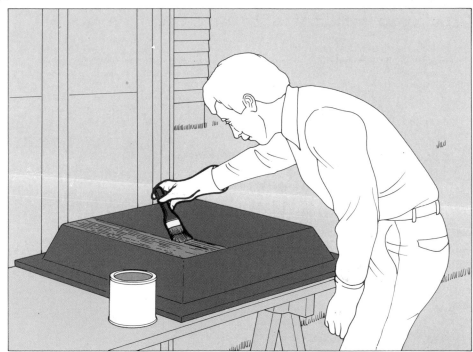

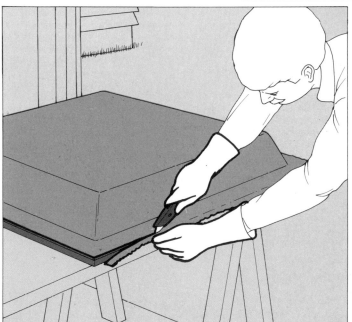

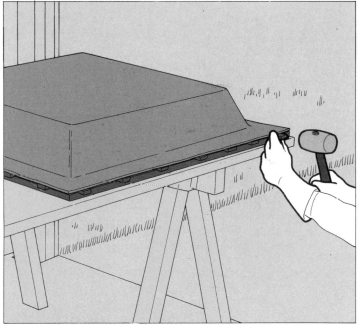

4 **Trimming the finished form.** When the final coat of resin has become rubbery (after about 45 to 60 minutes), cut away the excess laminate along the mould edge with a trimming knife; do not lift or bend the laminate. Let the laminate cure overnight or longer, following the manufacturer's instructions, in a warm, dry, dust-free place.

5 **Releasing the mould.** Insert thin wedges of wood or plastic between the laminate and the mould at 150 mm intervals. Tap the wedges gently with a mallet. If the laminate does not spring free of the mould, do not try to prise it loose. Instead, invert the mould and run warm water into it to melt the wax parting compound.

Finish the rough edges of the laminated basin by filing them with a forming tool, then sanding with 600 grit emery paper. Working from the inside of the basin, drill a drain hole with a carbide-tipped hole saw fitted in a power drill. Put a wood block under the drain-hole area while drilling, to avoid splintering the laminate.

Tracking Down Fibreglass Flaws

The many variables involved in fibreglass lamination can cause some problems in working with the resin and some flaws in the finished product. In most cases you can trace the source of the problem fairly easily and correct the damage.

Errors in measuring and mixing the resin can produce a resin mixture that does not harden. This may be the result of adding too much or too little hardener, or of using resin or hardener that is too old and no longer effective. If the resin fails to set on only part of the work, probably it has been unevenly mixed, or the mould or parting compound was not allowed to dry completely. If resin does not cure after three to five hours, you will have to scrape it off, thoroughly clean the surface, mix some new resin and begin again.

A workshop that is too cool can also delay curing: keep the temperature at 10°C or above. But a room temperature that is too high—above 30°C—can cause the resin to cure too quickly or to harden in the mixing pot before it is applied. Mixing too large a batch of resin can have the same result. Activated resin generates heat as it cures, and large quantities produce enough heat to make a significant difference in hardening time. Left open too long—about 45 minutes—a large quantity of activated resin may even begin to smoke, thus becoming a fire hazard.

Some errors are apparent only after the laminate has cured; they manifest themselves as shown in the photographs on the right. Most can be remedied by the application of a second gel coat over the surface. However, in the case of leaching, it is necessary to cut away the flawed area and replace it with a fibreglass patch *(page 109)*. The same is true of any area where the layers of glass fibre fabric separate—or delaminate—and are no longer solidly bound together with resin.

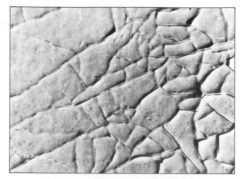

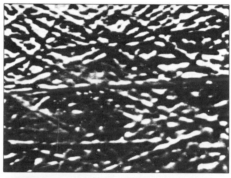

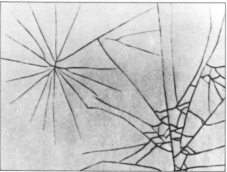

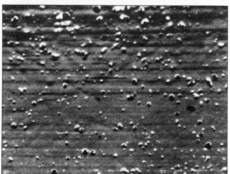

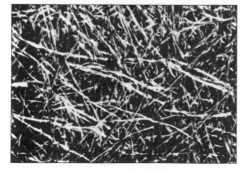

Common Surface Flaws and How They Are Caused

Crazing. Fine hairline cracks may appear in the surface immediately or as much as several months later. They are caused by incorrect proportions in the resin mixture or by the use of a laminating resin that is not compatible with the gel coat being used *(page 89)*.

Star cracking. Radiating cracks may become visible in the gel coat if it has been applied in too thick a layer or if the underside of the laminate receives a sharp blow.

Fibre pattern. A raised honeycomb effect on the laminate surface is the result of failure to use a layer of fine surface-mat glass fibre between the gel coat and thick woven roving. If the surface is smooth but the fabric pattern is visible, the gel coat is too thin or, in a moulded form—where the gel coat is applied first—the fabric was laid on before the gel coat was stiff enough.

Pinholing. A pocked surface results from the introduction of tiny air bubbles into the gel coat, usually during mixing. Bubbles are particularly difficult to see in a tinted gel coat. Also, if the gel coat is too viscous, the bubbles, though visible, are difficult to remove.

Leaching. Glass fibre fabric is left exposed when resin is washed away, either because it was improperly cured or because the resin used is not weatherproof. The fragility of the exposed glass in a leached area substantially weakens the laminate; the laminate should be patched.

Molecules Custom-Built to Serve a Specific Need

Most of the materials used for construction are nature's gifts and can be manipulated only within fixed limits. Woods can be seasoned and formed, metals tempered and alloyed, stone crushed and shaped, but the basic qualities of each material are inbuilt and unchangeable. Because they are synthetic, however, plastics can be tailormade: not only the end product but the very character of the substance itself can be shaped to suit the purpose in hand.

Leo Baekeland, a Belgian-born chemist working in New York, was the first scientist to create a truly made-to-order material—earlier versions of plastics, such as celluloid *(page 7)*, had all consisted of chemically treated natural substances. In 1907, while he was searching for a substitute for shellac, Baekeland mixed and heated two unpromising-looking liquids, phenol and formaldehyde, both smelly derivatives of coal. When his flask cooled, he found a resin which was both altogether unlike its ingredients and far superior to shellac. He had produced the first synthetic plastic, which was later named Bakelite in its creator's honour.

Today, such metamorphoses of familiar substances or their extracts into synthetics possessing durability and ease of shaping not to be found in nature have become commonplace. Most of them involve a few colourless gases and a volatile liquid or two derived from petroleum or from natural gas. Using a combination of heat, pressure, and catalysts (substances that hasten chemical change without taking part in it) industry converts such raw materials as these into the plastics that ease modern life.

The secret of these remarkable transformations, from Baekeland's first successful simulation of shellac to today's routine triumphs, is to be located in the invisible realm of molecular structure. A typical plastic molecule strings together many hundreds or even thousands of carbon atoms, each surrounded by a complement of other atoms. This chain of atoms, although at best it is only a minute fraction of a millimetre long, is a molecular giant.

In spite of their size and complexity, these giant molecules are relatively easy to assemble. Petroleum and natural gas provide molecules containing only a few atoms, mostly carbon and hydrogen, often arranged like very short sections of the immense carbon chains of plastics. The magic of technology can cause these short sections of chain to line up and fuse together end to end, each of them adding several links to the larger chain. In the language of science, each small molecule is called a monomer; the result of their linking, the unwieldy but invaluable plastic molecule, is a polymer.

In its simplest forms, the plastic polymer consists of a single kind of monomer, repeated hundreds or thousands of times over. Polyethylene, the waxy, pliant stuff of squeeze bottles, is a scrambled mass of such polymers. The monomers from which they are made are, as the name of the plastic indicates, molecules of ethylene gas.

Scientists can shape the properties of a plastic not only by choosing the monomers, but also by controlling the way the building blocks are arranged at the crucial moment when the monomers unite chemically to form the plastic polymers. In basic or so-called low-density polyethylene, for instance, a numerous array of side branches trail off from the main carbon chains. These branching polymer chains act as spacers, separating the molecules and reducing their natural tendency to cling to one another. This polyethylene is flexible and lightweight; it softens at moderate heat.

For a polyethylene that withstands higher temperatures, chemists have developed a way to assemble unbranched polymer chains. With no side chains to space them, these molecules pack more closely, cling together more tightly and make up a denser, less flexible plastic with greater heat resistance. Tougher still is a version with links between adjacent polymer chains. Made by drenching the plastic in high-energy radiation, these cross-links bind the molecules in a rigid matrix, giving the familiar squeeze-bottle polyethylene enough durability for aerospace applications.

The invisible intricacies of plastics. Each of the six-atom monomers in the polyethylene molecule *(below, far left)* has two atoms of carbon and four of hydrogen. Before they are strung together, these monomers make up explosive ethylene gas. But when thousands of them fuse together, they form a molecule of resilient plastic. Many-branched chains *(below, centre)* yield a pliant polyethylene that softens at 95°C. Linked in a latticework *(below, right)*, the same chains constitute a polyethylene that can withstand twice that temperature.

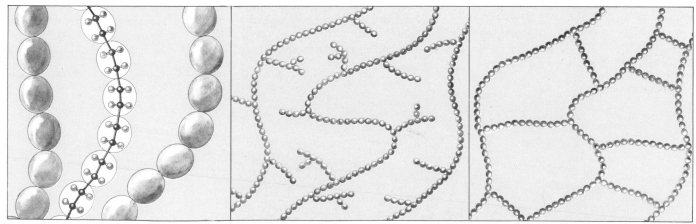

Laminated Surfaces Move Out of the Kitchen

The same plastic laminates that work so well in the kitchen and bathroom as easy-care coverings for worktops are equally useful in other rooms of the house, where their sleek surfaces can cover coffee tables, window sills and bookshelves. Mindful of this decorative potential, manufacturers are making the laminates in bold colours, ranging from bright scarlet to deep navy blue, in wood-grain patterns that faithfully reproduce the graining and colour of everything from light oak to Burmese teak; and even in simulations of hessian, slate and leather.

Laminates can be successfully applied over existing laminated surfaces and over virtually any smooth wood. One of their chief attractions is that they permit you to build pieces from inexpensive hardboard, chipboard or plywood. Laminates cannot, however, be applied over linoleum or ceramic tile without an underlayment of wood, although it is often possible to avoid this intermediate step by using laminated panels—large sheets of plastic laminate that come already bonded to hardboard.

Regardless of the surface to which they are applied, plastic laminates are usually fastened in position with one of two adhesives. Both technically are contact cements, which means that the cement is spread on two surfaces, and bonds immediately when the surfaces are brought together. One of these cements is water-based and easy to use; it is, in addition, non-toxic and non-inflammable but its bonding strength is low, so it is best used for large, flat surfaces. The other cement, far stronger, is petroleum-based and, like all such products, is hazardous. It is toxic, extremely volatile and explosive.

Before you open up a container of this petroleum-based cement, extinguish all smoking materials and pilot lights, and turn off the circuit breakers for fans, re-frigerators and other motor-driven equipment. Do not let the cement touch your skin, and avoid breathing its fumes. Work in a well-ventilated area, preferably outdoors, though outdoor temperatures can interfere with drying time. The cement bonds best at about 20°C. Hot weather may make it dry too fast, and in cold weather it may dry too slowly and become brittle. Either condition weakens the bond.

Both forms of contact cement are applied in the same way, with a paintbrush or a roller. Normally one coat is enough, but some wood surfaces—especially the end-grain of plywood—will soak up the cement and will require a second coat. When the cement has dried to the tacky point, the two surfaces are ready to be joined.

Use care in positioning the laminate, for once the two layers of cement have touched, it is virtually impossible to pull them apart. Edging strips and similar small pieces can usually be guided into place without any preliminaries, but bigger pieces may need prior alignment. Since the tacky cement sticks only to itself, you can keep the two surfaces separate during alignment by covering them with strips of wood or pieces of wax paper until they are properly positioned. As soon as the laminate is aligned, slip out the strips of wood or the wax paper and press the laminate into the adhesive with a roller of wood or hard rubber; alternatively, pass a block of wood over the laminate while repeatedly tapping the block with a mallet.

Laminates come in sheets 1220 mm wide and up to 2440 mm long; larger sheets are obtainable to special order. The standard sheet is 1.2 mm thick, but sheets 0.8 mm thick are sometimes used for surfaces that get little wear, such as the backs of cabinet doors.

A special laminate, called postforming grade, is useful for installations where the laminate is required to fit over a sharply curved surface. The paper layers in this laminate are not the usual heavy brown paper; instead, they resemble crepe paper. For wide curves, such as those on the edge of a round or oval table, postforming laminate can be shaped while it is cold. For tight curves, it must be warmed. In factories, where industrial heaters and presses are available, interior curves with a radius as small as 6 mm are possible; but when the laminate is heated at home, curves with a radius of less than 20 mm are impractical. To warm the postforming laminate, a hot-air gun, a tool normally used to remove paint, is ideal.

When applying a laminate to any surface, old or new, make sure the surface is scrupulously clean, smooth and dry. Sand down any rough spots and fill in any indentations with wood putty. If you are re-laminating over old laminate, cement any loose edges. Break any surface bubbles in the old laminate by hitting them with a mallet. Remove hardware, sinks and taps from kitchen and bathroom surfaces, and sand the old laminate to roughen its surface so that the cement will adhere better. Be sure, however, to clear away any chips or sanding dust. These would not only interfere with the bond but might also signal their presence in the form of lumps in the finished surface.

The laminate itself is frequently cut as much as 6 mm larger than the surface it covers and then trimmed to size after it is in place. The preliminary cutting techniques for plastics are described on pages 20–29. For a neater finish between two laminated surfaces that meet at right angles, the edge is usually bevelled. The trimming and bevelling operations can both be performed with an electric router or with hand tools—specifically, a flat metal rasp and a fine-cut file.

Seating a vertical edge. Brush an even coat of contact adhesive on the laminate and on the vertical surface being covered. When the adhesive is tacky, grip the edges of the laminate in both hands, nestling the edges in the last joints of your fingers so that your fingertips are free to use as a guide in aligning the top edge of the laminate with the top of the vertical surface *(inset)*. Then bring the two adhesive-coated surfaces together, pressing the laminate against the vertical edge, and roll the laminate with a small wooden or rubber roller until it is firmly seated.

Rounding a sharp curve. Apply an even coat of contact adhesive to the laminate and the surface being laminated; join them as far as the point where the curve begins, using the technique shown on the left. Then put on gloves and warm the laminate with a hot-air gun, holding the heat source just above the plastic. When the plastic is pliable—usually in about 30 seconds—pass it quickly round the curve and press it into the adhesive with a roller.

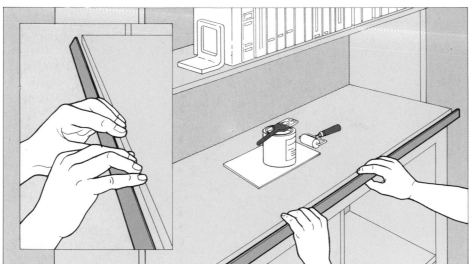

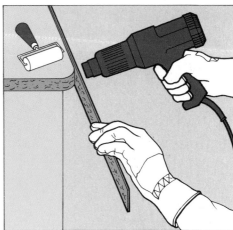

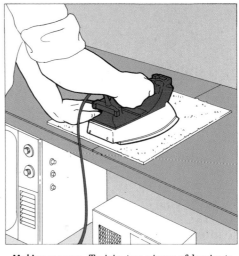

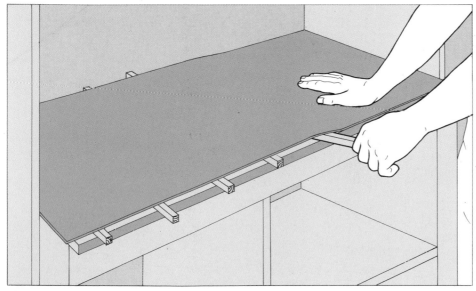

Aligning a large surface. Apply contact cement to the laminate sheet and to the horizontal surface being laminated, using a little extra cement round the edges. When the adhesive is tacky, lay wood strips at about 300 mm intervals across the horizontal surface; the strips should be at least 20 mm thick. Place the laminate in position on top of the strips. Starting at one end, remove the wood strips one at a time, pressing down the laminate as you go. When the two surfaces are joined, roll the laminate or, alternatively, use a block of wood and a mallet to set it firmly on to the horizontal undersurface.

Making a seam. To join two pieces of laminate, trim both edges to meet precisely *(pages 21–22)*. Apply contact adhesive to the laminate pieces and the surface being covered. Join one laminate piece to the base as shown on the left. Then align the second piece, beginning at the seam. Press both pieces into the adhesive, using a roller or a mallet and a block of wood to seat them firmly. To strengthen the seam line, cover it with a cloth and run a household iron over the plastic until it is warm to the touch; use the lowest setting on the iron. This will soften the cement, embedding the plastic more securely.

Choose an inconspicuous location for a seam. Do not allow the seam to run into an opening, such as the cutout for a sink. Avoid joining small sections of laminate; such seams have a tendency to pull away from the base.

Finishing the Edges of a Laminated Top

1 **Trimming an overhanging edge.** If the plastic laminate has been cut slightly larger than its base, remove the overhang with an electric router or a flat metal rasp. Fit the router with a flush-trim cutter, and pass the cutter along the overhanging edge *(below, left)*, shaving off narrow strips of plastic until the cutter's roller guide meets the vertical surface at a right angle to the top laminate *(inset)*. Then make one slow final pass, using the vertical surface as a guide, to cut away the last of the excess plastic.

When using a rasp *(below, right)*, cut away the excess laminate with light downward strokes. Hold the rasp at right angles to the edge of the laminate, but move it at a slight angle, covering 50 to 75 mm of overhang with each stroke.

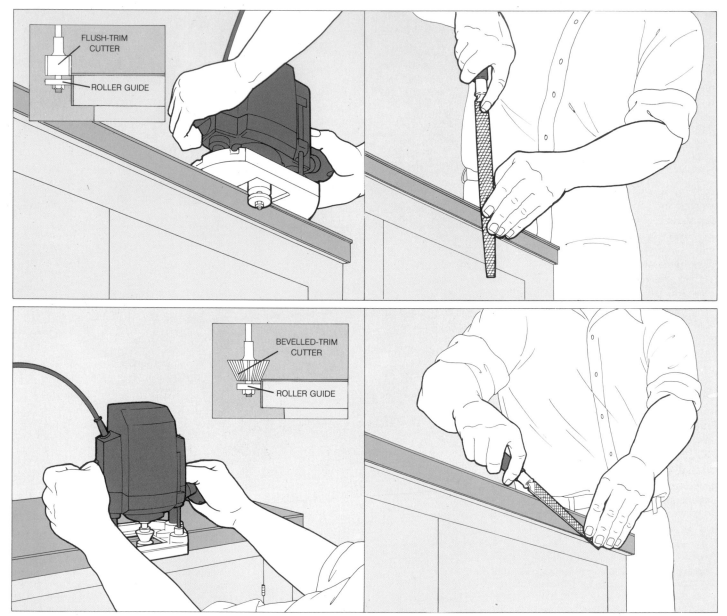

2 **Bevelling an edge.** Put a bevelled-trim cutter on the router and adjust the depth of the cut, setting the cutter so that the bottom edge of the blade falls just slightly below the bottom surface of the laminate being bevelled *(inset)*. Switch on the router motor, and when it reaches full speed, bring the cutter gently in contact with the plastic. Move the router along the edge in one smooth pass *(above, left)*, keeping the roller guide in constant contact with the vertical surface.

To bevel the edge by hand, use a fine-cut file, holding the file at about a 25-degree angle to the edge and moving it downwards in angled strokes that cover 50 to 100 mm at a time *(above, right)*.

Sheathing Three-Dimensional Objects

Laminated objects intended for less utilitarian purposes than kitchen worktops need some preliminary planning to ensure neat, unobtrusive joints. The beauty of laminates is only skin deep. When their patterned or coloured surfaces are cut, the core is exposed and will be visible as a dark line wherever two pieces of laminate meet at right angles. But there are ways to minimize these lines—by plotting the sequence in which the object is assembled and its surfaces are covered. The assembly of the parson's table on the right shows proper planning.

Before applying a laminate, first consider the angle from which the object will most often be viewed. The surface facing the viewer is the one that should be covered last. On a low table, for instance, the sides should be covered before the top. The dark line of the core will then face the sides of the table, where its presence will be less obvious. On the other hand, the sequence of placement should be reversed for a high shelf such as the mantel over a fireplace, because the top of the mantel tends to be in view less often than the sides.

The second consideration in planning neat joints is the nature of the surface over which the router's roller guide passes as the router trims or bevels laminated edges. The smoother this surface, the neater the bevelled or trimmed edge. Wherever possible, try to plan these finishing operations so that the router will move over the side grain of plywood or over a previously laminated surface. Running the router over plywood end-grain, with its bumpy surface, will create a wavy edge.

A Table Intended for Laminating

1 **Cutting the base and top.** Cut a square tabletop from 19 mm plywood. Cut two side pieces the same width as the top, and two end pieces 38 mm narrower. The end piece legs will thus be 19 mm narrower than the side piece legs, but the aprons of all four pieces will be identical in width. Lap the side pieces of the table over the end pieces and secure them with 50 mm panel pins. Then nail the tabletop to the resulting skirt assembly.

Cut eight plywood rectangles for the inside legs. Each rectangle should be the same height as the skirt assembly, but four should be as wide as the outside legs of the end pieces and four should be 19 mm narrower. Nail the wide and narrow rectangles together in pairs to form each L-shaped interior leg. Then join the L-shaped legs to the skirt assembly, nailing through the face of the skirt into the interior edges of the legs. Countersink all pin heads.

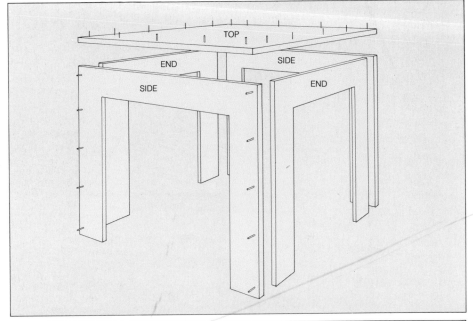

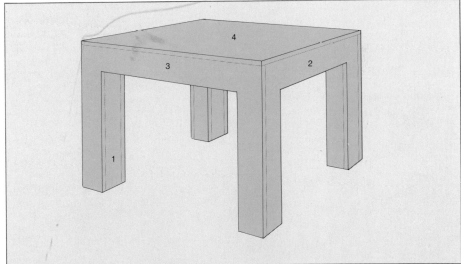

2 **Completing the lamination.** Using the techniques described on pages 96–97, apply laminate in the numbered sequence shown here. First cut eight rectangles of laminate to fit the inside surfaces of the legs. Trim the rectangles even with the bottom of the end and side skirts, and apply them to the insides of the legs (1). Then sheathe the end pieces of the skirt assembly (2), thus covering the end-grain of the plywood of the side pieces; trim the laminate to size either with a router or with a rasp and a file, as shown opposite. Next cover the side pieces (3), trim the laminate to size, and bevel the outside corner of each leg. Finally, apply a piece of laminate to the top (4), trim the laminate to size then bevel the top edges.

Convoluted cover-up. Colourless epoxy is swirled over a butcher's-block tabletop, protecting its surface while allowing the beauty of the grain to shine through. The pourable plastic, roughly the consistency of a thick syrup, will be smoothed with the edge of a plastic-covered card to form a moisture-proof, scratch-proof seal 3 mm thick. With successive applications, the coating can be increased to 6 mm without altering the colour or clarity of the material that lies underneath.

Patching, resealing and recoating are the inevitable by-products of having a home: no household surface takes care of itself. Exterior walls, roofs and pathways will weather, crack and change shape under attacks of wind, rain and temperature fluctuations. Interior walls, ceilings, floors and built-in fixtures must submit to nicks, scuffs and regular washings, not to mention an occasional blow that may be severe enough to cause greater damage.

In times past, such household repairs often took more time and effort than they were worth. It was easier to live with the scuffs and cracks than to fix them. When restoration was necessary, the work was frequently left to professionals, who possessed the specialized tools and equipment—and the years of practice—needed to do the job well. But plastics have changed all that. Today's easy-to-use synthetic fillers, caulking compounds, sealants and paints make most kinds of surface repairs and refinishing a simple and economical matter, even for the amateur. The same is true for the use of these materials on new work.

The qualities that set these plastics compounds apart from traditional materials are their superior powers of adhesion and their infinite shapability. True to their name, they can be formulated to respond to virtually any demands made of them.

Trowelled-on polyester metal fillers, for example, will bond to irregularly shaped holes and dents, eliminating the need for costly welding. Silicone and polysulphide caulking compounds will remain permanently pliant, outlasting their oil-based predecessors, which in time become brittle. Quick-setting synthetic fillers and coatings can be applied without special tools and are packaged in small quantities for household-sized jobs. With one-coat synthetic-rubber waterproofing emulsion, there is no need for expensive layer-over-layer built-up roofing. The fast-curing epoxy mortars and grouts are far stronger than conventional cement and plaster, and new plastic paints and varnishes cover any surface you are likely to want to finish or refinish. There is even an aquatic epoxy paint that goes on underwater, for redecorating swimming pools or fish ponds.

Properly applied, most of these synthetic fillers and paints produce surfaces more durable than the natural materials they cover. But when they are used to repair leaks and cracks, more than resurfacing may be required. Sometimes there are serious structural defects that must first be diagnosed and remedied. The success of the job will also depend on choosing the right coating, one that is compatible with the surface beneath, and on preparing that surface properly. These important preliminaries are discussed in this chapter, along with the techniques for applying the new plastic coatings.

Compounds to Patch Holes in Almost Anything

Plastic filling compounds are used to patch holes in everything from human teeth to motorcar bodies. Strong, fast-setting and resistant to water and chemicals, these components are ideal for a wide range of repairs about the home. Whether the job calls for filling a gouge in a kitchen work-top, patching a small hole in a water tank or shaping a replacement for a broken corner of a garden chair, the right plastic filler and application technique can produce a nearly undetectable repair in the damaged object.

The polyester or epoxy resins that are the base for such plastic filling compounds as wood putty or metal paste can be used in their clear form or mixed with filler materials and pigments to match almost any surface you may need to repair. The choice between epoxy and polyester should be based on the requirements of the job in hand. Epoxies are more expensive, but they are stronger, adhere better to many surfaces, and offer greater resistance to heat and corrosive chemicals. Unless these properties are essential, a polyester resin is usually sufficient; polyesters match epoxies in water resistance, are more tolerant of mixing errors, and cure more quickly. Problems of polyester adhesion can usually be overcome by simply roughening the surface or drilling anchor holes.

Both polyester and epoxy filling compounds are available either ready mixed or in multiple-component products. A ready-mixed filler, such as the familiar plastic wood putty, can be used directly from the tube or tin; the resin, hardener, filler and colour are already blended. Most such ready-mixed compounds are sold in small quantities and are practical for touching-up work or small repairs, although they are more expensive than the multiple-component filler.

The parts of a multiple-component filler must be precisely measured and mixed, following the procedures used for mixing casting plastics *(page 82)*. With certain of these multiple-component products, you add the hardener to factory-mixed resin and filler; with others, you add a factory-mixed paste of hardener and filler to the liquid resin. If the hardener and filler are in paste form, mix the paste first with a small quantity of resin to liquefy it and prevent lumps from forming when the rest of the resin is added to the mixture.

Some products require you to mix fillers and pigments with the resin before you add the hardener. Because of the increased potential for error with such a product, you should make trial mixtures before you mix the batch you will use on your repair. Pay particular attention to the proportion of filler material to resin. Too little filler will result in excessive shrinkage as the mixture cures; the addition of too much filler will make the mixture crumbly and reduce its adhesion properties.

Filling compounds can be matched in colour or other characteristics to a wide variety of surfaces by the addition of appropriate filler material. Metal powders, for example, can be used for cosmetic repairs as well as in applications where resistance to stress or friction is required. Use an aluminium filler if the repair will be subject to friction. Graphite powder added to a filler will have the effect of improving its sliding properties.

Non-metallic filler materials are also available, and these include ceramic powders, chopped glass fibre, and powdered stone. Fibreglass is an all-purpose filler that is also a strong reinforcement, which makes it useful for sheet-metal repairs. Since fibreglass is water-resistant when cured, it is well suited for repairing rust holes on such items as water tanks, gutters, steel panels, or even cars. If it is thinned with acetone to the consistency of paint, fibreglass resin can also be used to prime bare metal before further repairs are made with chopped glass or another filler.

Fillers of powdered ceramic, which have good insulating properties, are the best to use for repairs where heat or electricity is present. Such ceramic fillers can be readily tinted to suit your requirements by the addition of coloured powders, available at most paint or D.I.Y. shops.

For patching and repairing wood, many ready-mixed compounds are available in a variety of wood colours. These tinted fillers cannot be further coloured with stain; however, they can be retinted before they are applied to achieve the exact colour desired, or touched up with an oil-based paint after they have cured. You can avoid the necessity for this chore by mixing your own filler, using a polyester resin base and fine sawdust from the wood you are using. If you intend to stain such a mixture at the same time you are staining the surrounding wood, use a high concentration of sawdust in the filler, and brush the hardened patch with acetone to expose as much of the sawdust as possible prior to staining.

You will need a kitchen scale to measure the ingredients by weight, or a glass measuring cup if the ingredients are to be measured by volume. Use disposable cups and spatulas for mixing, or use glass and metal utensils that can be cleaned with acetone to prevent impurities from getting in the filler. Clean your paintbrushes with acetone between applications, or use very cheap brushes and discard them after they have been used for this purpose.

An electric drill is handy when you are preparing a surface for repairs. Fitted with a sanding disc, it can be used to remove paint or corrosion quickly; with a burr bit, it can be used to grind a feathered edge round a hole. Masking tape and paraffin wax are needed to contain the filler and to protect the surrounding surface from possible damage by solvents.

To put a smooth surface on the filler, you will need to cover it with a sheet of clear plastic household wrap, which will not stick to the filler. To polish a finished repair, use a buffing disc with a plastic-polishing compound *(page 104)*.

Tips on Safe Handling

Because almost all of the chemicals in plastic fillers are volatile and somewhat caustic, you must take care to ensure adequate ventilation and avoid naked flames. Keep a fire extinguisher nearby and use plastic gloves and protective eye goggles to prevent accidental contact with the materials. If any resin does get on your skin, wash the affected area immediately with soap and water. Keep a supply of eye-wash accessible in case resin gets in your eyes. Before opening any of the filler containers, read the manufacturer's safety information and familiarize yourself with the remedies prescribed.

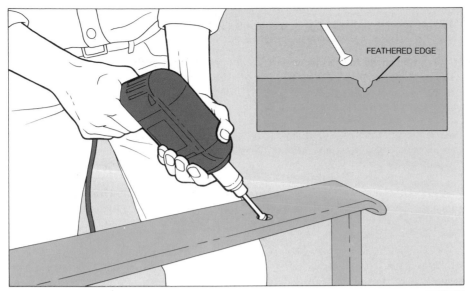

FEATHERED EDGE

A Nearly Invisible Patch for a Small Hole

1 Preparing the hole. With a burr attachment on an electric drill, feather the edge of the hole at a shallow angle to a distance of 6 mm *(inset)*. Use the drill's cooling fan exhaust to blow loose particles and dust from the hole.

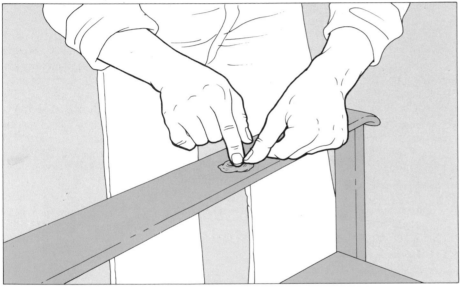

2 Making a wax dam. Shape a bit of paraffin wax with your fingers to build a 3 mm dam round the hole, slightly outside the feathered edge. Do not let the wax touch any part of the hole; it would stop the filler from sticking.

3 Filling the hole. In a shallow dish, mix sufficient filler to fill the hole, then use the mixing spatula to drip filler into the hole. Tamp the filler with the spatula to force out any air bubbles. Then add filler until it is about 1 mm above the undamaged part of the surface.

4 **Trimming off the excess.** When the plastic filler has partially hardened (usually in about five minutes), use a sharp, wide-bladed filling knife or scraper or a single-edged razor blade in a holder to shear away the wax dam and the excess filler flush with the surface. Avoid gouging the filler or the wood beside it with the corner of the blade.

Discard any leftover filler and clean the tools with acetone. Mix a small batch of fresh filler.

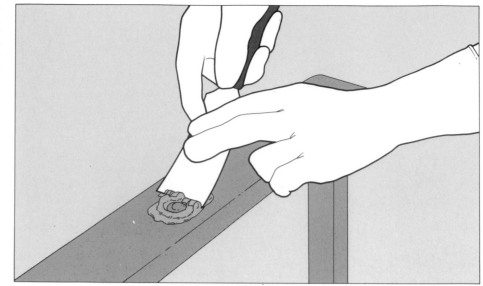

5 **Finishing the filler.** Drip a small amount of filler on to the repair and cover it with a piece of clear plastic wrap. Spread the filler evenly by lightly smoothing it with a single-edged razor blade drawn across the film. Remove the film and allow the filler to cure for two to five hours, according to the manufacturer's instructions.

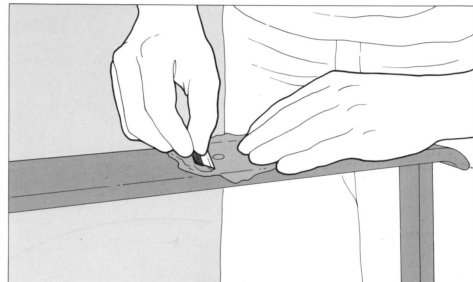

6 **Buffing the repair.** After lightly hand-sanding the patch with 400 grit emery paper, spread rubbing compound on a buffing attachment for an electric drill and buff the patch, applying light pressure and a circular motion. Continue until the patch blends into the surrounding surface.

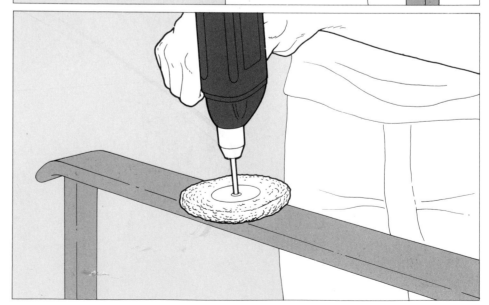

Stopping a Crack and Sealing It with Filler

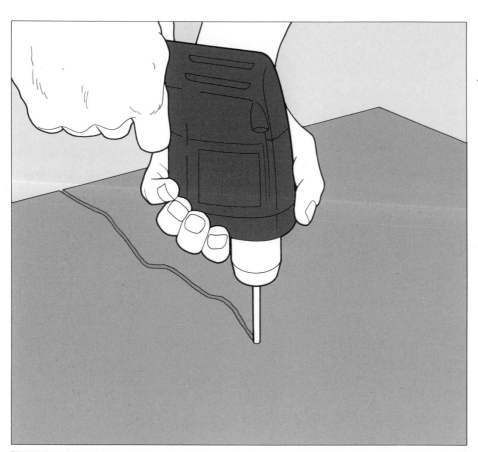

1 **Drilling to stop the crack.** Drill a hole 6 mm in diameter through the cracked plastic surface to relieve the tension that is creating the crack. When you do this, use the end of the crack as the centre point of the hole.

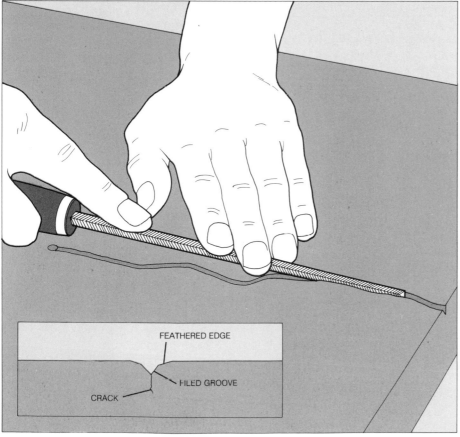

FEATHERED EDGE

FILED GROOVE

CRACK

2 **Widening the crack for filler.** Use a small triangular file to enlarge and deepen the crack, making a V-shaped groove at least 3 mm deep. Feather the edges of the grooves slightly *(inset)*, and clean out all loose particles and dust. If the crack follows a straight line, cover up the undamaged surface with masking tape extending right to the feathered edges.

3 **Filling the crack.** In a shallow dish, mix sufficient plastic filler to fill the filed groove, then apply the filler with a putty knife, working across the groove. Build up the filler about 1 mm higher than the original surface. When the filler has partially hardened, remove the masking tape if used and complete the repair as shown in Steps 4 to 6, page 104.

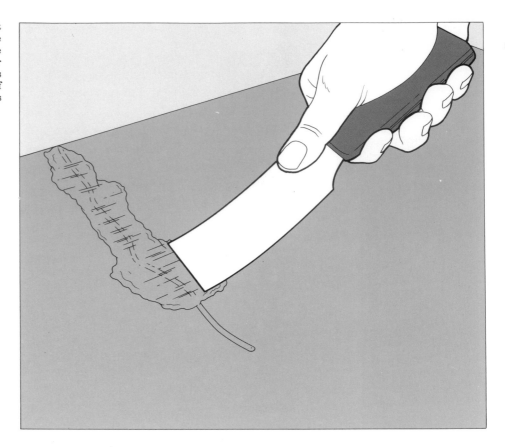

Anchoring Filler in a Sheet-Metal Dent

1 **Stripping paint from the surface.** Remove paint and other protective coatings from the damaged surface, using an electric drill fitted with a wire-brush attachment. Using heavy pressure and a slow, sweeping motion, expose shiny metal across the entire damaged area and 25 mm more of the surrounding surface in all directions. Use either detergent and water, or alcohol to clean and de-grease the stripped metal.

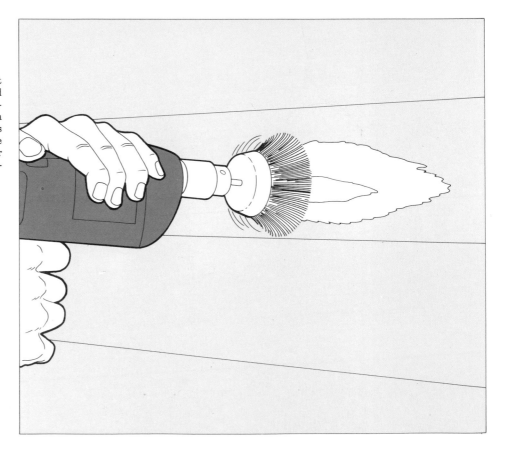

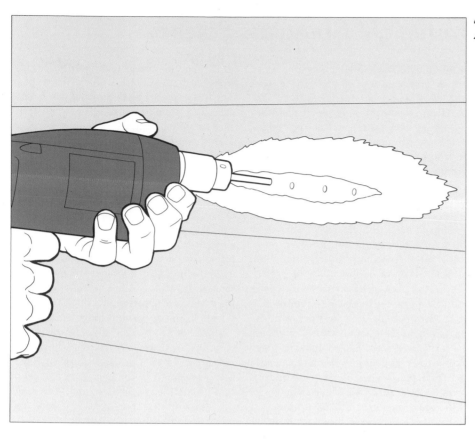

2 **Drilling anchor holes.** Drill 6 mm anchor holes about 25 mm apart within the damaged area to offer a good grip for the filler. Paint a thin primer coat of polyester resin over all bare metal.

Cover the area around the primed surface with masking tape. When the primer is no longer tacky, fill the dent with polyester filler *(Step 3, opposite page)*. Let it cure, then sand it smooth and paint it to match the surrounding surface.

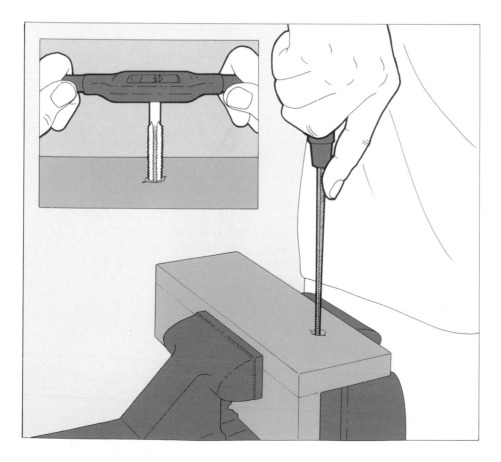

Renewing Stripped Threads with an Anchored Plug

Preparing the hole. Remove the damaged threads by drilling out the hole with a bit one and a half times the original diameter of the hole. Use a small triangular file *(left)* to cut several notches in the side of the hole; these notches, which should be at least 3 mm deep, will prevent the filler plug from rotating. Clean the hole and degrease it with alcohol, then fill it as shown in Step 3, opposite, using a filler that matches the colour of the surface.

Allow the filler to cure completely (this will generally take from about two to five hours), then redrill the hole through the filler plug to the original diameter. Cut new threads in the new hole with a tapping tool *(inset)*.

Watertight Fibreglass Patches

A gaping hole in a plastic, metal or wood surface that once was smooth and watertight does not necessarily spell disaster. Using a variation of the fibreglass-lamination techniques shown on pages 88–94, you can apply a strong, watertight patch to anything from a plastic bin to a fibreglass roof panel. Careful sanding, finishing and tinting can make most such repairs virtually undetectable.

Both the polyester and epoxy resins used in working with fibreglass will also bond well with wood and metal. However, polyester's relatively short drying time, low cost and easy workability make it preferable to the more expensive epoxy-based resins; the latter adhere more readily but are harder to use because they are so thick. For most household repairs, the best choice is a pre-accelerated, two-component polyester resin with a liquid hardener, available from plastics suppliers, and marine hardware and motor accessory shops.

Fibreglass repairs are based on the same principles as fibreglass lamination: overlapping layers of resin-impregnated cloth form a solid surface across the damaged area. Careful mixing of the resin compound ensures proper bonding between the layers of glass and the material being patched. A gel coat applied to the working side of the patch creates a smooth, waterproof surface. (Components and mixing techniques are discussed on page 82.)

Most resins are mixed with 3 per cent hardener by weight. Cool weather slows curing; if necessary, you can increase the proportion of hardener to 5 per cent to speed curing, but be aware that excessive hardener can cause brittleness by curing the resin too quickly. In some cases you may be able to speed curing by warming the area of the repair with a heat lamp. If repairs are urgent in temperatures below 10°C, you can use a technique known as cross-hardening, which allows curing at temperatures as low as freezing point. This technique involves first mixing the standard hardener into the resin, then adding a second hardener containing benzoyl peroxide. Ask for specific information on proportions if you decide to purchase materials for cross-hardening.

To get a strong patch, you must prepare the surrounding surface carefully. Make sure it is free of loose particles, dirt, paint and grease. If the surface is metal, scrape round the hole with a wire brush until the metal shines, then degrease the metal with soap and water, alcohol or vinegar. When the metal is dry, prime it with a thin coat of plastic filling compound (page 102).

Since resin-saturated glass fabric is slippery and awkward to handle, it is convenient to soak the glass fibre in resin, then transfer it to the repair on a sheet of clear plastic household wrap. This stops the glass fabric from coming apart and minimizes dripping.

Because fibreglass work is messy and stray resin is extremely difficult to remove if given time to cure, use disposable containers and utensils if possible. Otherwise, clean the equipment between steps with acetone or another recommended solvent. Cover the floor and surfaces adjacent to the work area with sheets of newspaper to catch any drips.

Most of the components used in fibreglass work are irritants. In fact, both the resin and the hardener are caustic, inflammable and toxic, and benzoyl peroxide is particularly dangerous. Use them only in a well-ventilated area, away from flame, and keep them away from skin and eyes. Always wear a respirator and goggles when you cut or sand fibreglass, since fine glass fibres will be released in the air.

A Two-Sided Patch for a Plastic Container

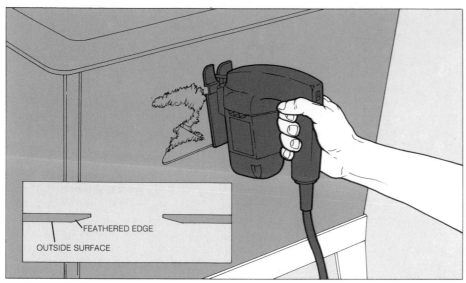

1 Cutting out the damage. Use a jigsaw with a metal-cutting blade to remove damaged material. Make the hole a regular shape to simplify patching. Use a sanding block with 80 grit sandpaper to remove loose particles from the edges of the hole you have cut.

On the outside surface of the container, feather a 50 mm bevel round the hole *(inset)*, using an electric drill with a sanding disc fitted with 80 grit paper. Cut a piece of cardboard slightly bigger than the hole, cover it with plastic wrap, and then tape it to the inside of the container so that the plastic wrap is facing the hole.

FEATHERED EDGE

OUTSIDE SURFACE

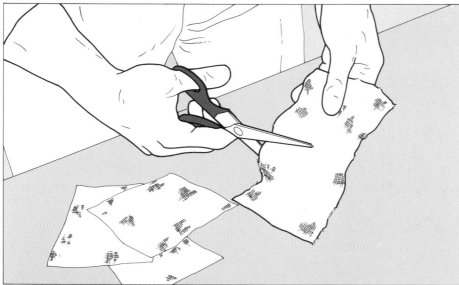

2 Cutting the patches. Cut a piece of glass fibre cloth large enough to cover the hole and the 50 mm feathered area, then cut a piece of glass fibre mat slightly smaller. Continue cutting alternate pieces of cloth and mat, each slightly smaller than the last, until the total thickness of the cut pieces equals the thickness of the container wall. The final piece should extend about 25 mm beyond the hole on each side. Fray the ends of the glass fibres at the edge of each piece so that they can be pressed flat.

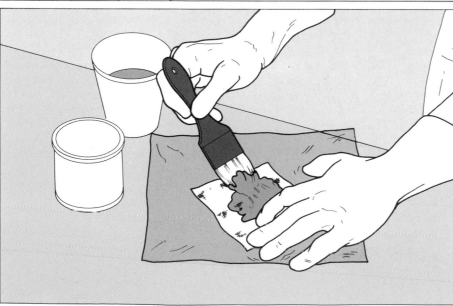

3 Saturating the glass fibre. Lay the largest piece of glass fibre cloth on a sheet of plastic wrap, mix the resin and hardener, and use a soft-bristled brush to saturate the cloth with resin. Work with a dabbing motion to avoid wrinkling the cloth. Centre the largest piece of glass fibre mat on the cloth, and dab the mat with resin until it is saturated. Continue to add alternating layers of the glass cloth and mat until you have built up the thickness that you need. Pick up the sheet of plastic wrap and transfer the patch to the outside of the hole, centring it over the opening and pressing it gently into place.

4 **Pushing out air bubbles.** With the plastic wrap still in place, use a plastic or rubber spreading tool to press air bubbles—which appear as white spots—out of the patch, working from the centre to the edges. Let the resin cure for several minutes, then carefully peel away the plastic wrap. Allow two to five hours for the patch to cure, then remove the cardboard backing.

Use an electric drill with a sanding disc to make a shallow depression in the patch on the inside surface of the container, feathering the edge 50 mm beyond the original hole. Cut pieces of glass mat to fill the depression, ranging from the size of the original hole to 25 mm larger on each side. Cut two pieces of glass cloth the size of the feathered area round the hole.

5 **Applying the inside patch.** After protecting the undamaged surface round the hole with paper and masking tape, mix a new batch of resin and paint the sanded area with it, then apply the smallest piece of mat. Saturate the mat by dabbing on more resin with a brush. Repeat this process with successive layers of mat, then with the final pieces of cloth, using the brush to force out air bubbles in each layer before applying the next. The final layer should be slightly higher than the original surface of the container. Lay a piece of plastic wrap over the entire patch, then press out any remaining air bubbles, working from the centre outwards.

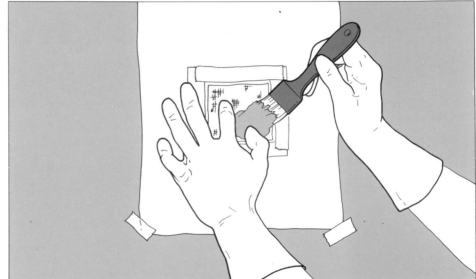

6 **Trimming the patch.** When the patch has partially hardened, carefully peel away the plastic wrap, then use a trimming knife to cut away any loose edges or stray strands. Do not lift up the patch or otherwise disturb the smoothed area.

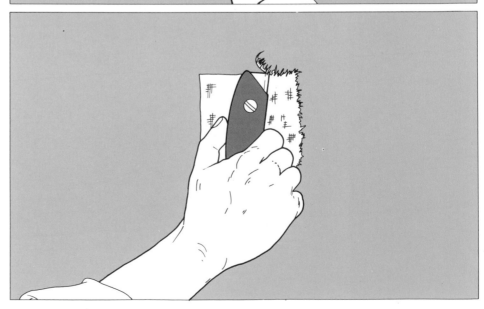

7 **Applying the gel coat.** Mix a gel coat *(page 89)* and use a soft-bristled brush to apply an even coat over the patch. Cover the gel coat with plastic wrap and press out air bubbles, smoothing gently from the centre towards the edges. Let the gel coat harden completely, then gently peel away the plastic wrap.

Lightly hand-sand the gel coat, using a fine-grit wet and dry paper covered with fibreglass rubbing compound. Brush on a second gel coat in the same manner as the first, allow it to cure, and then polish the area with a buffing wheel and rubbing compound *(page 104, Step 6)* or a liquid household abrasive.

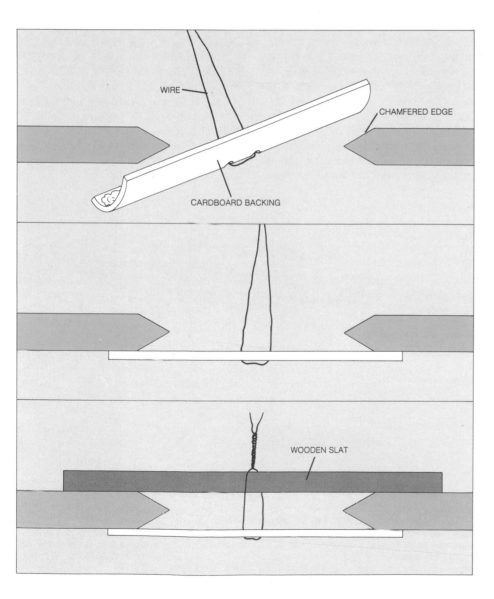

WIRE

CHAMFERED EDGE

CARDBOARD BACKING

WOODEN SLAT

A Supported Patch for a Hard-to-Reach Place

Attaching backing from the front. To secure a fibreglass patch in a hole that is accessible from only one side, you will need to glue a piece of cardboard to the inside surface. With a bastard-cut mill file, chamfer the edges of the hole on both sides, so that the hole is bordered by sharp edges. Then cut a piece of cardboard to overlap the chamfered area by 12 mm on all sides. Use cardboard flexible enough to bend through the hole but still retain its shape. Pierce two holes about 5 mm apart in the centre of the cardboard and thread a thin length of flexible wire through the holes. Apply a thin bead of quick-drying contact cement round the edge of the cardboard, on the same side as the loose ends of wire. Bend the cardboard slightly and then push it through the hole *(left, above)*.

With the cardboard centred behind the hole, pull the wire so the cemented edges are against the inside surface round the hole *(left, centre)*.

Place a wooden slat over the hole and twist the wire over the slat to hold the cardboard in place while the adhesive is drying *(left, below)*.

When the adhesive has dried, snip the wire and pull it out. Apply a layer of resin-soaked glass cloth inside the hole, tucking the edges into the space between the cardboard and the chamfered edge of the hole. Allow the resin to cure, then complete the patch as shown in Steps 5–7.

A New Generation of Buffered Sealants

Polymers, the stuff of plastic resins, have infiltrated the manufacture of such age-old sealing agents as mortars, grouts and caulks—in some cases a polymer fortifies existing formulas, and in others it replaces the older material altogether. Most modern caulks are made completely of plastics; mortars and grouts still largely consist of cement, sand and water. But modified mortars and grouts supplement the standard versions and are useful where greater strength is needed.

The toughest of the fortified mortars is one that has an epoxy added—it is about three times stronger than conventional mortar. It is also more resistant to the elements and adheres to timber, a property that permits stone flooring to be laid over timber rather than over a concrete slab. For patching concrete, epoxy-fortified mortar is superior to conventional mortar.

Epoxy-fortified mortar has three ingredients: a liquid resin, a liquid hardener and a cement-sand powder. All are available from builders' merchants and hardware shops. The two epoxy components are mixed first, then the mortar powder is added; proportions of powder to epoxy mix are specified by the manufacturer.

Working with epoxy mortars requires the same tools as for ordinary mortar—a bucket for mixing in, a stirrer and a notched trowel—with the addition of rubber gloves to spare your hands possible irritation from the epoxy. The methods of working are also the same, except that epoxy mortars set faster than ordinary mortars. Mixed, they have a pot life of about three hours; spread, the mortar must be topped by brick or stone in about 20 minutes, or a skin will form across the top of it, rendering further cementing impossible.

Latex, another plastic resin added to mortar, yields a product about twice as strong as conventional mortar and midway in cost between epoxy mortar and the conventional type. It is noted for its resistance to moisture and to cracking caused by vibration. But unlike epoxy mortar, it does not adhere to wood. Sold in two parts—a liquid resin and a cement-sand powder—latex mortar is mixed and applied in the same way as epoxy mortar.

Latex-based additives are also used to fortify grout, the cement mixture that is trowelled between tiles or stone, giving this product advantages that latex gives to mortar: greater strength and resistance to water. Translated into practical terms, this means fewer repairs and easier cleaning. Latex grouts are usually sold as a pre-mixed powder to which water is added; check the label information before you buy, and choose a grout with a relatively high latex content if you are grouting bathroom or other tiles in wet conditions.

Plastic sealants, like their predecessors, the linseed-oil-based colloids, are available in tube and rope form, as well as in tins and caulking-gun cartridges. Applied to outside surfaces, especially places where dissimilar materials meet, modern sealants of this kind do a better job of keeping out weather and insects.

Of the many sealants on the market, the most common *(chart, opposite page)* are acrylic latex, butyl, polysulphide, polyurethane and silicone. The acrylic sealant is most effective when used indoors. The butyl will provide a durable outdoor seal, and more durable still are the last three, called elastomers because of their rubber-like properties. Unfortunately, some of these elastomers will shed paints that are unable to flex readily under temperature changes, but to make painting unnecessary, they come in various colours.

Working with Resin-Fortified Materials

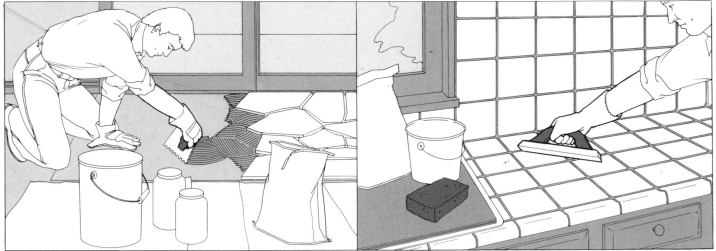

Using resin-impregnated materials. Clean the work area and assemble the tools and materials you need. Mix the mortar or grout according to the manufacturer's instructions (here, the mortar is an epoxy type), and trowel out enough to last for about 10 minutes of work. For mortar, spread the mixture with a notched trowel held at a 45-degree angle *(above, left)*. For grout, spread the mixture with a rubber float held at a 45-degree angle, forcing the grout into the spaces between the tiles *(above, right)*. Use a finger to press grout into corners. Let the grout dry for five to 10 minutes, then wipe the tile with a wet sponge. Rinse the sponge often in a bucket of water, but do not pour the grout-filled water in a sink or bath; the grout may clog the drain. Let the tile surface dry until a haze appears, then buff the tile with a crumpled piece of nylon.

Common Sealants and How to Use Them

	Durability	Adhesion	Tack-free	Solvent	Comments
Acrylic latex	2 to 10 years	Good	¼ to ½ hour	Water	Not recommended for outdoor use or on metals.
Butyl	7 to 10 years	Excellent	½ to 1½ hours	Naphtha, white spirit	For use mainly on masonry; high moisture resistance; shrinks slightly as it cures; principal colour grey or black.
Polysulphide	20 years	Excellent	24 to 72 hours	Toluene, TCE, MEK	Requires recommended primer on masonry; available in aluminium colour for use on double glazing.
Polyurethane	20 years	Excellent	24 hours	Toluene, white spirit, MEK	Relatively easy to apply; requires recommended primer on metal.
Silicone	20 years and up	Excellent	1 hour	Toluene, Xylene, white spirit	Excellent around baths and outdoors on glass and metal; requires primer on masonry.

Ranking sealants. The chart above shows common kinds of plastic sealants along with their main distinguishing features. Listed horizontally, the sealants are rated for durability and adhesion, and for the length of time they take to lose their initial stickiness, which indicates how long they stay workable. Also given with each listing is the solvent needed to smooth or clean the sealant; the final column shows special factors governing the use of a given sealant. All the sealants are available in colours, all but the latex sealants are suitable for outdoor work and, in general, the longer lasting the sealant, the higher its price. The solvents abbreviated are trichloroethylene (TCE) and methyl ethyl ketone (MEK).

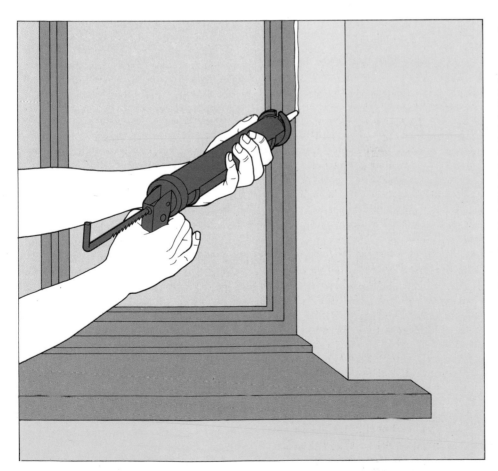

A Simplified Seal Done with a Caulking Gun

Applying the sealant the right way. Before beginning the operation, check the condition of the surface to be sealed; except when you are using latex sealant, which can be applied on a damp surface, the area should be clean and dry. Also check the cartridge label for special instructions covering such situations as working in cold weather or over unprimed surfaces. Then prepare the cartridge: cut off the nozzle at a 45-degree angle and puncture the inner seal by pushing a long nail into the nozzle. Hold the caulking gun against the work at a 45-degree angle and pull it towards you, pumping the trigger. The bead of sealant should overlap both of the edges of the crack. Smooth the bead with a solvent-soaked cloth.

When sealing deep cracks, stuff foam rubber or old newspaper into the crack before applying a finishing layer of sealant.

Plastic-Based Coatings: Paint for Any Purpose

Except in works of historic restoration, where paints based on linseed or tung oil are still used, most modern coating materials are made from plastics; alkyd and latex-based paints are practically universal for exterior house painting, and latex is the standard choice for interior work. In addition, a great array of fluid resins, from synthetic rubbers to two-part epoxy coatings, make it possible to coat not just wood or plasterboard or masonry, but virtually any surface in or on your house.

You can, for example, give a factory-like finish to all plastic, metal or ceramic fixtures, from kitchen-range hoods to bathroom sinks, with polyurethane, vinyl or epoxy coatings that will dry either to an ultrahard sheen or to a rubbery, grease-resistant hide. With virtually no preliminary preparation, you can convert slabs of rough wood—such as rough planks or slices of tree trunk—into attractive tabletops by coating them with a thick, tough, crystal-clear layer of a specially formulated epoxy resin. And tool handles dipped in a rubber-based compound instantly acquire slip-proof, cushioned grips.

Outside the house, shingles or timber cladding can be covered with flexible alkyd coatings that expand and contract with temperature changes. Clear silicone will protect brick walls from the ravages of moisture. Oil-resistant, fast-drying acrylic toppings sheathe drives; skidproof compounds based on synthetic rubbers can protect the surfaces of garden paths and steps and make them less hazardous to walk upon when the day is rainy.

Of course, no single resin can offer every advantage of today's modern coatings. Yet so versatile are plastic resins that there is usually a selection of coatings for a given job. Making your choice from among the available products is the first crucial step in any painting or sealing job.

To guide you in this choice, the box below lists the major families of coatings and indicates the results that each one delivers. Consult the list to see which products seem likely to serve your needs; then, having narrowed your choice, consult the chart opposite to see which of these are compatible with the surface that is to be covered. If the surface has previously been painted, you should also consult the chart on page 116 to find out which of your choices will be compatible with the old coating.

Despite the sophistication of modern plastic paints, primer coats are usually required and are particularly important when painting plastic or metal surfaces. Follow the manufacturer's instructions concerning the primer for each paint.

Pros and Cons of Frequently Used Finishes

Included in this guide are the major families of plastic-based coatings. The descriptions include only those properties offered by the product in its most common form. Many large paint shops also carry special formulations—such as polyurethane floor coatings with admixtures of non-skid chips.

☐ ALKYDS. Available clear or in colours, alkyd-based paints cover easily and are economical. They adhere well to most surfaces except fresh concrete and plaster. Alkyds are durable under normal conditions but deteriorate with excessive exposure to detergents, solvents and corrosive chemicals.

☐ EPOXIES. These coatings are produced by a chemical reaction between an epoxy resin and a hardening agent, mixed together before application. The mixture retains its working consistency for 15 minutes to four hours; excess cannot be saved. Epoxy paints, available in all colours, adhere excellently to wood, metal or masonry. They form tough, hard coatings that can withstand abrasion, solvents, detergents and corrosive chemicals, although colours can fade in strong sunlight when used on exterior surfaces. High price limits epoxy to jobs where high performance is a must.

☐ LATEXES. Latex paints, which are commonly sold as vinyl silk matt or emulsion paints, are economical and very easy to apply; in addition, they are non-inflammable. These paints will resist fading and stand up to light abrasion and corrosion. Latex films breathe, so they resist blistering, but they require thorough surface preparation for good adhesion.

☐ POLYURETHANES. Coatings of this type cure hard, glossy and tough, with excellent chemical and abrasion resistance. But polyurethanes are highly inflammable until they dry, and they are expensive. Because they contain solvents that attack existing coats of alkyd or latex paint, they cannot be applied over those coatings. Clear polyurethane darkens with long exposure to sunlight.

☐ SILICONES. Dilute solutions of silicone resin will shield unpainted masonry surfaces against moisture without changing colour or appearance. Higher concentrations may be combined with alkyds and aluminium or carbon pigments to produce stove enamels that will withstand temperatures up to 650°C.

☐ SYNTHETIC RUBBERS. Chlorinated-polyisoprene, polystyrene butadiene, polyvinyl toluene and other resins, i.e. synthetic rubbers, all form the basis for many water-resistant coatings. Available in a moderate selection of colours, such rubber-based paints seal and decorate swimming pools and masonry; they are a good choice for walls that are subject to condensation or frequent washing. Also in this family are bituminous paints used for waterproofing roofs, walls or areas of new concrete.

☐ VINYLS. Resins derived from polyvinyl chloride and polyvinyl acetate produce flexible coatings with exceptional durability and resistance to water, corrosive chemicals and abrasives. Most commonly available in combination with alkyd resins, vinyl coatings are ideal for metal and masonry surfaces in marine use and where chemical resistance and good appearance are important.

Matching the Paint to the Stresses It Will Face

Material	Use	Environment	Resin	Alkyd	Epoxy	Latex	Polyurethane	Silicone	Synthetic rubber	Vinyl
Wood	General purpose	Interior		●		●	●			●
		Exterior		●		●	●			●
		Exterior/marine		●						●
	Heavy duty	Interior		●	●	●	●			●
		Exterior		●						●
		Exterior/marine		●						●
	Floors	Interior		●						
		Interior/high abrasion		●			●			
Metal	General purpose	Interior		●						
		Interior/high humidity			●		●	●		
		Exterior		●						
	Heavy duty	Exterior/marine			●		●		●	●
		Exterior/corrosive			●		●			●
	Floors and stairways	Interior		●	●		●			
Plaster and plasterboard	General purpose	Interior		●		●				
		Interior/high humidity		●					●	
Masonry	General purpose	Interior		●		●	●			●
		Interior/high humidity			●		●		●	●
		Exterior		●		●		●	●	●
	Heavy duty	Exterior/marine			●			●	●	●
		Exterior/corrosive		●	●					●
	Floors	Interior		●			●			
		Interior/high humidity		●			●			
		Interior/heavy traffic		●			●			
Glass	General purpose	Interor		●	●	●				
Plastic	General purpose	Interior		●	●					

Choosing a paint. Surfaces vary not only in material but in the kind and amount of punishment they must take; the three columns on the left of this chart are in effect a job description of the project. "Heavy duty" describes a surface that must be frequently washed or is subject to abrasion. "Marine", "high humidity" and "corrosive" refer to environment—the first to coastal areas with salty air; the second to places subject to dampness, such as bathrooms; the third to urban areas, where the air may have high proportions of smoke and acidic gases. Find the line for your project, then read across to the coating column on the right. A dot under a coating means it is acceptable for the job.

Preparing a Compatible Surface for Paint

Plastic-based paints, no matter how superior their credentials, will perform well only on a surface that has been properly prepared. The surface must provide a strong base for the new coating. If it has weak spots or is rough or uneven, follow the steps on pages 103–113 to reinforce, smooth and fill it. After this stage, preparation varies according to the type of surface and whether it is already coated.

If the surface has been painted or sealed previously, first make sure that the coating you are planning to apply is compatible with the old coating (chart, below, right). Once you know that the coatings are compatible, roughen any glossy areas of the old paint with sandpaper or steel wool. Flaking or peeling paint must be taken off completely; handscrapers, hot-air guns and chemical paint removers are good for this job. Large exterior metal and masonry surfaces, such as wrought-iron fencing and brick walls, can be cleaned with power tools—sandblasters for metal, waterblasting equipment for masonry, both of which it is possible to hire.

Surfaces that are to be painted for the first time must always be scrupulously clean. First remove all traces of grease and oil from wood with mineral spirits. Seal knots that may ooze sap with knotting solution, which is readily available at D.I.Y. or paint shops.

Metal surfaces are best cleaned with acetone or lacquer thinner, or with one of the more expensive commercial degreasing compounds. Less costly alkaline cleaning agents—strong detergents and trisodium phosphate—are also effective; however, these cleansers should be dissolved in hot water—65° to 95°C.

Steel and iron must also be stripped of any rust. Treat light rust with phosphoric acid in gel or solution form, available at hardware and paint shops. Not only do they clean away rust, they also etch the metal surface to increase paint adhesion. For serious rust, chip or scrape away the loose scales with a wire-brush attachment on an electric drill or with a wire brush and a hand-held scraper.

Bare concrete and masonry block surfaces present two special problems. The porous types are very difficult to clean properly—dirt and grime settle deep into crevices and can cause paint to blister or peel. Smooth, glazed masonry, on the other hand, provides a difficult surface for any new coating to penetrate.

To clean masonry, a stiff brush and strong detergent can be effective, but a high-pressure spray-cleaning device—obtainable from tool-hire firms—will save considerable time; it can pump a strong jet of water to blast grime off a pathway or a wall. Once clean, bare masonry should be treated with a solution of dilute hydrochloric acid to etch the smooth glazed surfaces and provide a key for the coating. Hydrochloric acid will also dissolve efflorescence, a powdery alkaline substance that sometimes crystallizes on masonry. Afterwards, rinse the surface with water to remove the acid. All masonry should be allowed to weather for as long as possible before it is painted; freshly poured concrete needs 60 to 90 days to release its alkalinity.

Plastic surfaces, though smooth, usually do not need to be roughened for good adhesion. Static electricity, however, can sometimes cause paint to crawl on plastic surfaces—especially acrylic sheets—and must be removed with an alcohol wash (opposite page, below). If the object being painted is portable, an electrically earthed metal screen placed underneath the plastic will help to keep it static-free while it is being painted.

Surface preparation can be tedious and messy. When working with caustic cleaning agents, wear a hat, rubber gloves and old clothes. Wear a dust mask for fine-sanding projects, and put on goggles and a charcoal-cartridge respirator before using hydrochloric acid indoors. Ventilate your work area well; also, before you start work, clear away or cover anything that could be damaged by accidental spills.

Making a Chemical Match with Paint Over Paint

Existing surface	New coating					
	Alkyd	Epoxy	Latex	Polyurethane	Synthetic rubber	Vinyl
Alkyd	●	○	●	○	○	○
Bituminous (roof coating)	○	○	●	○	●	●
Cement paint	○	●	●	●	●	●
Epoxy	○	○	○	●	○	●
Latex	●	●	●	○	●	●
Oil	●	○	●	○	○	○
Polyurethane	○	○	●	●	○	○
Silicone	○	○	○	○	○	○
Synthetic rubber	●	○	●	○	●	●
Vinyl	●	●	●	○	●	●

Recoating an old surface. To determine whether a new paint can safely be applied over an existing paint, read down the first column to find the current surface paint. Below each possible new coating listed across the top, a solid dot indicates compatibility. An open dot indicates that the pairing is not recommended. If you do not know what kind of coating is currently on the surface, experiment with a small amount of the new coating in an inconspicuous place.

An Acid Scrub for Stains

Cleaning masonry. Use a wire brush to remove loose efflorescence. Then, wearing goggles, rubber gloves and protective clothing, paint on a solution of 1 part dilute hydrochloric acid to 9 parts water mixed in a plastic, not metal, bucket. To avoid dangerous foaming and splattering, always pour the acid into the water, never the water into the acid. Apply the solution to the masonry with a natural bristle scrubbing brush, using plastic dustsheets, if necessary, to keep the solution off everything except the masonry. When the acid has stopped bubbling, rinse the surface thoroughly with clean water.

Draining Static Electricity

Ridding sheet plastic of static electricity. Loop one end of a bare copper wire through a piece of wire mesh and attach the other end to an electric earth, such as a metal cold-water pipe. Place the mesh on the worktable, under the plastic sheet, and wipe the plastic with an anti-static liquid or perspex cleaner. Although any soft cloth can be used to wipe on the liquid, a well-wrung chamois will result in the least spotting.

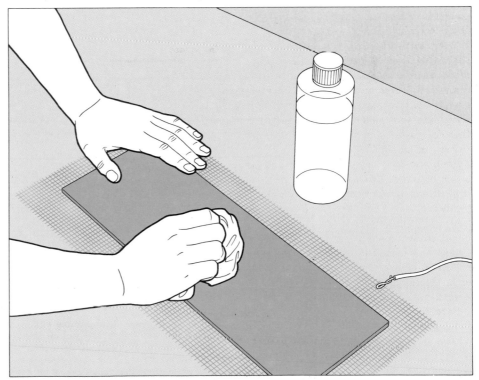

The Fine Points of Application

Plastic-based coatings vary widely in both consistency and composition. Some are watery-thin for fast spreading; others are soupy for a textured finish. Some are made with water for easy cleaning up, and others with volatile solvents for quick drying. The variety of forms in which plastic-based coatings are produced has also spawned a broad range of application techniques.

Brushes, of course, are the standard tool, but some coatings require natural bristle brushes, whereas synthetic bristles work better for others. For general-purpose coatings, such as alkyds, use a natural bristle brush of good quality. Latexes demand nylon or polyester brushes, which do not get soggy in water. Fast-curing, high-gloss epoxies and polyurethanes—often applied to metal or very smooth timber—are best spread with disposable sponge brushes. And there is a special nylon-bristled exterior or concrete brush that simplifies the job of working both latex and alkyd coatings into the cracks and crevices that appear in rendering and brickwork.

The correct way to use the paintbrush also varies with the type of coating you have chosen to apply. Alkyds and latexes should be brushed thoroughly—first back and forth, then crosswise. Synthetic rubber coatings, in contrast, should be brushed on with two or three strokes—just enough brushwork to spread them evenly. Clear polyurethane coatings should be spread carefully on to the surface, as slowly and deliberately as possible.

For large surfaces, rollers spread coating films more smoothly and rapidly than brushes. A fully loaded 225 mm roller can hold enough paint to cover over a square metre of surface. Like brushes, however, rollers have to be matched to the coating being applied. For example, sheepskin, natural or artificial, is unaffected by solvents, so it is suited to volatile epoxies and polyurethanes. On the other hand, the fibres of sheepskin are likely to mat, and even fall out, after contact with alkaline latex paints. Rollers can also be bought in foam sponge, either plain or textured for decorative finishes. Use the chart below to choose the right roller for your work.

Specialized applicators for hard-to-cover surfaces include paint pads, which are helpful for areas too confined for the use of rollers, and sheepskin painting mittens, which are used for wiping paint on to thin posts and rails. Some coatings are formulated to be applied without any tools at all; they are simply poured on to a surface. Or in some cases, the object to be coated is just dipped and allowed to drain.

Fitting the Roller Fabric to the Paint

| Coating | Surface | | |
	Smooth	Textured	Rough
Alkyd	Sheepskin (short nap)	Acrylic	Acrylic
Epoxy	Sheepskin (short nap)	Sheepskin (medium nap)	Sheepskin (long nap)
Latex	Polyester	Polyester	Polyester
Polyurethane	Sheepskin (short nap)	Sheepskin (medium nap)	Sheepskin (long nap)
Silicone	Sheepskin (short nap)	Sheepskin (medium nap)	Sheepskin (long nap)

Choosing the roller fabric. To match a roller to a painting job, consider both the paint and the surface. The fabric of the roller cover must spread a paint evenly without reacting to its resin. It also must travel over a surface of a particular texture without matting or falling apart. Use this chart to determine the recommended roller fabric, then choose a nap suitable for the surface you are painting. Generally, longer naps are best suited for rough surfaces and short naps for smooth.

Special Tools for Special Situations

Coating rough surfaces. To work paint into the cracks and crevices of a coarse surface, use an exterior brush with nylon bristles that are not only thicker than ordinary bristles, but split, or flagged, at the ends to carry more paint. Dip the brush squarely into a pan or roller tray containing about 12 mm of paint. Work it over the surface with an up, down and sideways motion.

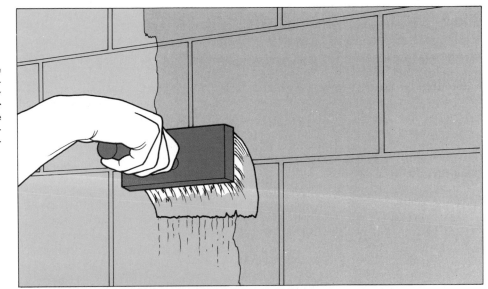

Applying an ultra-glossy coating. To stop brush marks from showing on a mirror-smooth surface, use a sponge brush rather than a bristle brush. Submerge about half the sponge in the paint, then paint with short, steady strokes, taking care to allow only the bevelled tip of the brush to come in contact with the work.

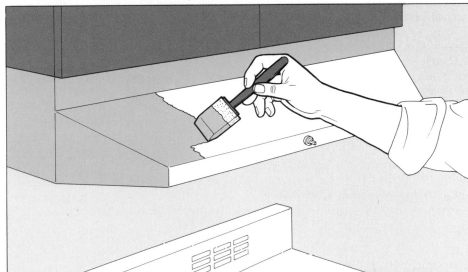

Painting awkward surfaces. Pipes and railings, tedious to paint with a brush, can be coated very quickly using a sheepskin mitten. Dip the palm of the mitten directly into a paint tray and then wipe down the pipe or railing *(right)*. A plastic liner in the mitten stops the paint from staining your hand, and the mitten can be cleaned for reuse in the same way as a roller. The same mitten can be worn on either hand.

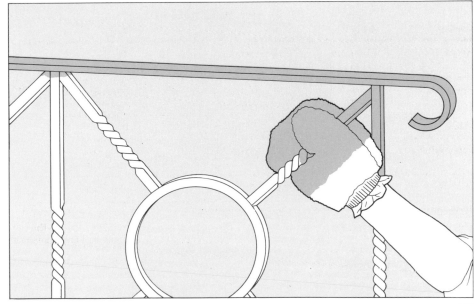

The Pour-On Polymer Coatings

1 Combining the components. Mix equal parts of resin and hardener in a disposable calibrated paper cup. Stir the batch thoroughly but gently with a clean wooden stirring stick, taking care not to introduce air bubbles. After two minutes of mixing, pour the thick coating over the surface to be covered—here, a butcher's block tabletop—working in a spiral from the outside in.

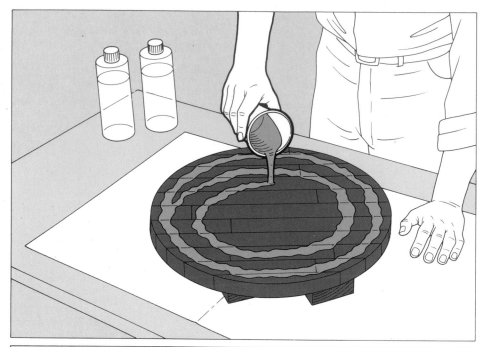

2 Smoothing the coating. Using a plastic-covered playing card as a spreader, distribute the coating evenly over the surface. Allow some of the coating to run over the edge, as in icing a cake; smooth this edge coating with a disposable sponge brush. Prick any large bubbles with a toothpick, then snare stray bits of lint with tweezers. While the coating is soft, blow gently on the surface through a drinking straw—the carbon dioxide that you exhale will break any tiny surface bubbles.

When the coating is completely dry, in two to three days, add additional layers if desired, until the coating is as much as 6 mm thick.

Dipping to Sheathe a Handle

Sheathing an object in plastic. Suspend the object to be coated on a length of twine or wire, and slowly lower it into a can of rubber-based vinyl plastic coating compound. Withdraw the object slowly, about 25 mm every five seconds, and hang it to dry. Immediately seal the open can; escaping vapours could soften the sheathing, causing it to drip or sag. After about 20 minutes, dip the object a second time. Then allow the sheathing to dry thoroughly to a tough, pliable finish; this will take about four hours.

Spraying the Professional Way

The versatility and adaptability of plastic-based paints and sealers suits them to the fastest of all application techniques: spray-painting. With a portable spray gun, it is possible to apply a uniform, mirror-smooth coating more quickly than with a brush or a roller, or by any other manual method.

Virtually any large surface, from fine wood to coarse cinder block, can be spray-painted. Small surfaces and trim can be sprayed if carefully masked, but for very small areas the time needed for masking may exceed that saved by spraying.

Equipment for spray-painting ranges in complexity from disposable, albeit expensive, aerosol cans, which deliver a fine coating mist for small finishing projects, to high-capacity compressor-driven spray guns that can be hired from equipment hire shops. Between these extremes lies a tool that can perform almost all of the jobs handled by compressor-powered units, and with a real saving in paint: the lightweight airless sprayer. Conventional sprayers use compressed air to create a misty mixture of paint and air. The airless guns employ a small but powerful electric pump to propel only droplets of paint out through their nozzles, yielding more precise application and far less overspray than compressor-driven sprayers.

Before you begin painting with an airless sprayer, familiarize yourself well with its operation. Because models differ from manufacturer to manufacturer, read the manual supplied with your sprayer—and note the safety precautions in the box on the right. Then, if you have never spray-painted before, fill the spray gun with water and get the feel of using it by spraying newspaper hung vertically.

Although virtually any plastic-based coating can be sprayed, it must usually be diluted before it is used *(page 122)*. Most sprayers require paint about 25 per cent thinner than brushing consistency. The paint must also be free of impurities. If you notice any floating skin or dirt, filter the paint through twice-folded cheesecloth. Remember, too, that careful surface preparation is just as important when you are spraying as for any other method of application *(page 116)*.

In addition, spray-painting calls for extra caution in preparing the surfaces that you do not wish to paint. Because atomized paint can get picked up by air currents and drift a considerable distance—especially if you are spray-painting out of doors—protect the nearby surfaces with dustsheets and newspapers held in position with lengths of masking tape.

Finally, whenever you finish using a spray gun, clean its mechanism by flushing it with a solvent compatible with the paint that was sprayed.

The Safe Use of Hazardous Equipment

Airless sprayers must be treated with the utmost respect. Typical models spray at pressures as high as 207 bar, enough to actually force paint through your skin. When you are operating a spray gun, never point it at yourself or at anyone else. And never put your hand near the nozzle of an operating spray gun, not even for a moment.

Should you accidentally inject paint under your skin, get medical help immediately. Note the resin and solvents of the paint you were using, so that the doctor or hospital can determine the proper treatment.

To prevent accidental fires, do not smoke in a room where you are spraying solvent-thinned paints or paints whose base resins are inflammable; these include polyurethanes, epoxies and vinyls. Extinguish any gas pilot lights in the room. To guard against electric sparks, make sure that any extension cord you use is properly earthed. Before painting, put on a face mask and goggles and, when painting indoors, provide for adequate ventilation. Keep a fire extinguisher on hand at all times.

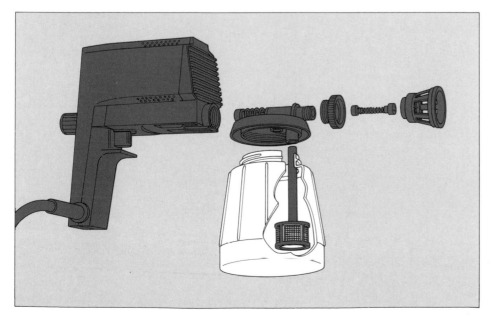

The airless sprayer. The motive force for an airless spray gun comes from a powerful electromagnetic motor. Turned on and off by a trigger switch—and regulated in velocity by a control knob on the rear of its insulated housing—the motor drives a spring-loaded piston back and forth. The moving piston sucks paint from the container, through a mesh filter and suction tube, to the cylindrical paint chamber, and then forces the paint from the chamber, past the spring-loaded spray valve and out through the nozzle, whose tiny orifice directs minute droplets of paint towards the surface being coated.

For large painting jobs, the small paint container shown here may be removed and an extended exhaust suction tube fitted directly to the nipples on the bottom of the paint chamber. The long tube, fitted with a clip and a filter, is then immersed directly in a large bucket of paint.

Preparing paint and sprayer. Dip a viscometer, which commonly comes with an airless sprayer, into the paint. Lift the cup, and time how long it takes for the paint to drain out through the hole in the bottom; compare this time with the time the sprayer manufacturer recommends. If necessary, mix in a small amount of the proper solvent, then test the consistency again. Continue thinning and testing until the paint runs out through the hole within the time recommended.

Filter the paint through cheesecloth if necessary, and pour it into the paint container of the sprayer, filling the container. Aim the gun at newspapers taped to a wall, and adjust the control knob until the paint sprays out in a uniform wedge-shaped pattern. Spattering paint indicates that the velocity is set too low; paint running down the paper indicates too high a setting.

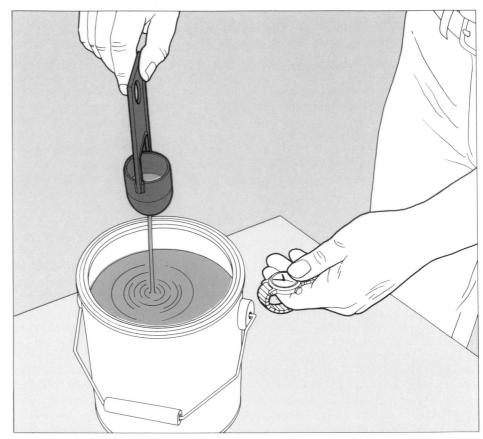

A proper indoor spraying set-up. To guarantee a safe and neat job, small surfaces you do not wish to coat should be covered with strips of masking tape. Shield larger areas with dustsheets. Wear a mask and goggles when spraying, and install a fan in the nearest window to draw away fumes. If you are far from a window, carry fumes to it by rigging up a plastic tumble-drier duct and a hood from the fan to the work area. Keep a fire extinguisher on hand—either a carbon dioxide or a dry chemical one.

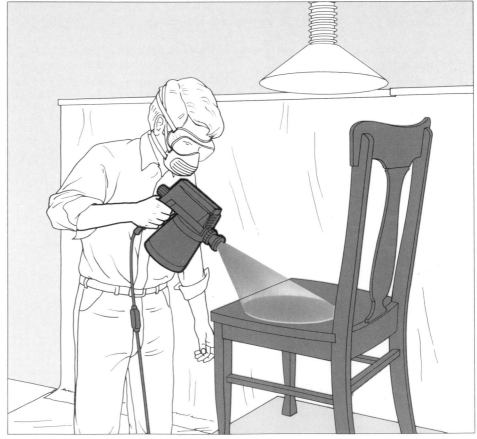

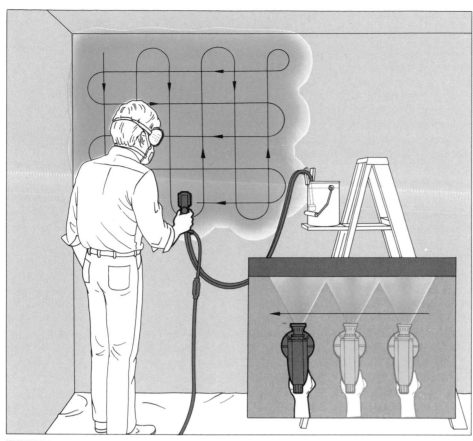

Spraying walls. For large jobs, supply paint to the sprayer through an extension tube rigged up to a large paint container. Hold the gun horizontal to the wall surface and, while spraying, move your entire arm up and down or left and right, keeping the nozzle about 200 mm from the wall *(inset)*; do not swing your arm in an arc, which would vary the distance of the nozzle from the wall, bringing it closer at the centre of each sweep, farther at the ends. Large, smooth walls are best covered with a crosshatch pattern, the paint applied first with vertical passes, then horizontal ones. For walls that are divided horizontally by mouldings, use overlapping horizontal passes only. A spotlight directed at the surface being sprayed will enable you to check that the paint coverage is even.

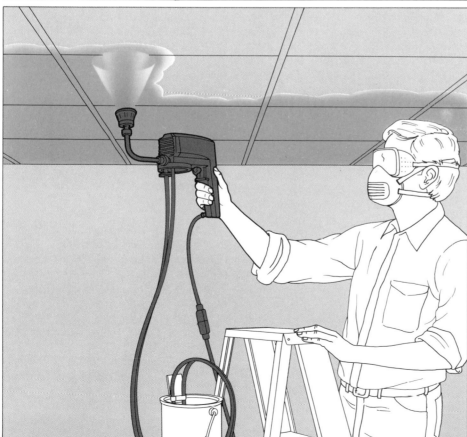

Coating horizontal surfaces. To paint ceilings or floors, replace the usual nozzle with a flexible extension nozzle. The extension—available for most airless sprayers—is made of soft copper tubing that you can bend with your fingers, thus aiming the spray up or down at horizontal surfaces without making it necessary for you to tip the gun or aim it directly overhead.

Picture Credits

The sources for the illustrations in this book are shown below. Credits for the illustrations from left to right are separated by semicolons, from top to bottom by dashes.

Cover: Fil Hunter. 6: John Elliott. 11–19: John Massey. 21: Frederic F. Bigio from B-C Graphics. 22–25: Oxford Illustrators Ltd. 26: Frederic F. Bigio from B-C Graphics—Oxford Illustrators Ltd. 27: Oxford Illustrators Ltd.—Frederic F. Bigio from B-C Graphics. 28, 29: Frederic F. Bigio from B-C Graphics. 30: Oxford Illustrators Ltd. 31: Frederic F. Bigio from B-C Graphics. 33: Walter Hilmers Jr. from HJ Commercial Art—Oxford Illustrators Ltd.—Oxford Illustrators Ltd. 34: Walter Hilmers Jr. from HJ Commercial Art—Oxford Illustrators Ltd. 36, 37: Arezou Katoozian. 38: Arezou Katoozian—Oxford Illustrators Ltd. 39: Arezou Katoozian. 40: Fil Hunter. 42–45: Eduino J. Pereira from Arts and Words. 47–51: William J. Hennessey Jr. 52–55: John Massey. 57: Oxford Illustrators Ltd.—Oxford Illustrators Ltd.—John Massey. 58: John Massey—Oxford Illustrators Ltd. 59–61: Oxford Illustrators Ltd. 62, 63: John Massey. 64, 65: Oxford Illustrators Ltd. 66: Fil Hunter. 69–73: Arezou Katoozian. 74: Oxford Illustrators Ltd. 75: Arezou Katoozian. 76–81: Walter Hilmers Jr. from HJ Commercial Art. 83–87: Eduino J. Pereira from Arts and Words. 90–93: Frederic F. Bigio from B-C Graphics. 95: John Martinez. 97: Elsie J. Hennig; Oxford Illustrators Ltd.—Elsie J. Hennig. 98: Oxford Illustrators Ltd. 99: Elsie J. Hennig. 100: Fil Hunter. 103–107: Frederic F. Bigio from B-C Graphics. 109–111; Stephen A. Turner. 112, 113: Elsie J. Hennig. 117: Frederic F. Bigio from B-C Graphics. 119: Frederic F. Bigio from B-C Graphics—Frederic F. Bigio from B-C Graphics—Oxford Illustrators Ltd. 120–123: Frederic F. Bigio from B-C Graphics.

Acknowledgements

The editors wish to thank the following: Edna F. Ashley, Fort McNair, Washington, D.C.; Charles Bender, Hyattsville, Maryland, U.S.A.; Ray Bender, Hyattsville, Maryland, U.S.A.; Louis Block, Minneapolis, Minnesota, U.S.A.; Kate Cann, Potton, Bedfordshire; Peter Casson, London; L. Davis, Uxbridge, Middlesex; François Delau, Paris; Frank Devlin, H. B. Fuller, Palatine, Illinois, U.S.A.; Dow Chemical Co., Freeport, Texas, U.S.A.; Stephen Draper, Greenbelt, Maryland, U.S.A.; Elizabeth Durfee Hengen, Winchester, Massachusetts, U.S.A.; Charles Hughes, Fairfax, Virginia, U.S.A.; Robert Kirkpatrick, Twinsburg, Ohio, U.S.A.; Jack Klarquist, Houston, Texas, U.S.A.; John Lawrence, New York; Susan Layden, Oakland, California, U.S.A.; William Mazzerela, Philadelphia, Pennsylvania, U.S.A.; Maureen Migdalen, New York; Don Morris, Manassas, Virginia, U.S.A; Jules R. Panek, Yardley, Pennsylvania, U.S.A.; Read Plastics, Rockville, Maryland, U.S.A.; The Rohm and Haas Company, Philadelphia, Pennsylvania, U.S.A.; Sally Rowland, Thaxted, Essex; Larry Russell, Philadelphia, Pennsylvania, U.S.A.; Robert Sellers, Gillette, New Jersey, U.S.A.; Shell Oil Co., Houston, Texas, U.S.A.; Specialty Products Company, Jersey City, New Jersey, U.S.A.; Strux Corporation, Lindenhurst, New York; Jody Swisher, Minneapolis, Minnesota, U.S.A.; Thermoset Plastics, Indianapolis, Indiana, U.S.A.; Brian Tyack, Alexandria, Virginia, U.S.A.; Will Wharton, Freeport, Texas, U.S.A.; D. Wildman, Wollaston, Northamptonshire.

Index/Glossary

Included in this index are definitions of some of the technical terms used in this book. Page references in italics indicate an illustration of the subject mentioned.

Abrasives, for polishing plastic, 35
ABS, 12; adhesives for, chart, 47
Acetal, 12
Acid scrub, for stains on masonry, *117*
Acrylic, 8, 12; adhesives for, chart, 47; bending, *33*; bending into irregular shapes, *34*; breaking with body leverage, *22*; casting from, 82; cutting with band saw, *23*; drilling, 30; joining with acrylic cement, 46, *51*; protecting from scratches, 32; removing scratches from, *38*; scoring and snapping, 20, *21*; shaping with heat, 32
Acrylic latex sealant, 112; how to use, chart, 113.

Adhesives: choosing, chart, 47; preparation before using, 46; types of, 46. See also Bonding, Solvent cementing
Alkyd paints: applying, 118; covering old paint with, chart, 116; pros and cons of, box, 114; rollers for, chart, 118; usage, chart, 115. See also Paints
Armature: *framework for reinforcing a clay mould*; 75

Baekeland, Leo, 95
Bakelite (the first synthetic plastic), 95
Band saw, 20; blades for, chart, 22; contouring with, *25*; cutting foam with, *29*; cutting round stock with, *25*; with fences, *23*
Bevelled edge, forming with power saw, *24*
Bits, for drilling plastic, 30
Bolt hole, drilling *31*
Bonding, with acrylic cement, 51; butt joints, *48, 51*; corner joints, *49*; methods of, 46; preparation of plastic for, 46; with solvent dip, *49–50*. See also Solvent cementing
Brushes, for applying plastic-based coatings, 118, *119*
Buffer, mechanical, 35, *36*; sheepskin, *36*
Buffered sealants, 112. See also Sealants
Buffing, 35, 36; chart, 35; inside curved surface, *37*; when removing scratches, *38*; repaired patch, *104*
Butyl, 112; how to use, chart, 113. See also Sealants
Buying plastics, 11

Carpenter's steel square, *16*; and marking complex shapes, *19*
Casting, in a mould, 82; finishing off, 87; hollow, in rigid mould, *85–87*; mixing compounds, box, 82; resins for, 82;

124

shrinkage, 82; solid, in flexible mould, 83–84. See also Moulds

Caulk, polymer-fortified, 112; using with caulking gun, 113

Cellulosics, 12; adhesives for, chart, 47; drilling holes in, 30

Cement, see Adhesives

Charcoal-cartridge respirator: *face mask with a replaceable cartridge that filters out noxious vapours*; 67, 82

Circular saw, 20; blades for, chart, 22; cutting laminate using, 27–28

Cleaning: plastic, 39; surfaces to be painted, 116

Combination square, 15, 16, 17

Compasses, 15, 18

Counterboring, 30, 31

Cracks, mending and sealing, 105–106

Cutting plastic: with band saw, 23; with body leverage, 22; chart, 22; foam, 29; interior cut, 28; laminates, 20; preparation for, 15; saws for, 20; techniques for, 20; tools for, 20

Cylinders: drilling holes in, 31; heating to shape, 32, 34; levelling, 16; marking straight cut lines on, 18; sawing, 24, 25; testing for squareness, 15; welding together, 55

Dipping, to sheathe in plastic, 120

Dividers, for marking plastic, 15, 18

Drilling plastic: bits for, 30; counterboring, 30, 31; precautions when, 30; preparation for, 15; with wood bit, 31

Electric carving knife, shaping foam with, 29

Epoxy, 12; casting from, 82; with fibreglass repairs, 108; in filling compounds, 102. See also Fillers

Epoxy-fortified mortar, 112

Epoxy paints, applying, 118; covering old paint with, chart, 116; pros and cons of, box, 114; rollers for, chart, 118; tools and brushes for, 118; usage, chart, 115. See also Paints

Fasteners, in joinery: hinging with pins, 44; nut and bolt, 45; rivets, 43; tap wrench, 45; types of, 42; wood screw, 44

Fence: *adjustable guide on a power cutting tool*; on band saw, 23

Fibreglass: *woven or felted glass fabric embedded in a plastic resin*; cleaning, box, 39; cover for table, 90–91; different glass fabrics for, 88–89; flaws in, causes of, 94; making, 88–89; shower base, making mould for, 74–75

Filing: to level cylinders, 16; prior to polishing, 35; to smooth inside curved surface, 37; to square edges, 16, 17; uneven edges, 17

Filled plastics, see Reinforced plastics

Filler rod: *plastic rod that softens when heated to join two plastic surfaces*; sealing butt joint with, 58–59; in speed welding, 61; in T-weld, 59; in welding, 56, 57

Fillers: fibreglass, 102; mending dent in sheet metal with, 106–107; mixing, for wood repair, 102; multiple-component, 102; patching with, 109–111; patching small hole with, 103–104; powdered ceramic, 102; ready-mixed, 102; renewing stripped threads with, 107; sealing crack with, 105–106; watertight, 108

Foam plastics: cutting, 29; marking for cutting, 15

Forstner bit, 30

Frame: *container in which an original model is secured before a mould is poured*; making mould for, 69–71

Fumes, 8, 32; from adhesives, 46; released when casting plastics, 67; when laminating fibreglass, 89; from PVC. See also Safety

Gel coat: applying on patch, 111; colouring, 88; in fibreglass lamination, 88–89; and flaws in fibreglass, 94; on laminated table, 91; on shower base, 93; for waterproofing fibreglass patch, 108

Glass fibre fabrics, 88–89; covering table with, 90–91; and shower base, 92–93

Glass fibre reinforced plastic, see Fibreglass

Glues, see Adhesives

Graph paper patterns: for plastic shapes, 19; for scoop, 19

Grout, latex, 112; using, 112

Heat: bending acrylic sheet with, 33; forming thermoplastic threads, 44; hems and seams in film, 62–63; precautions and pitfalls, 32; shaping laminates with, 96; shaping plastics with, 32; shrink tubing, 65; shrink wrapping, 64–65; welding, 52–61; welding joints, 41. See also Hot-air gun

Hems, in plastic film, 62–63

Holes: patching, 60, 102, 103–104; polishing drilled, 38, 39

Hot-air gun: for bending plastics, 32, 33; for bending PVC pipe, 34; shrink tubing, 65; shrink-wrapping, 64–65; welding joints, 41, 52

Hotplate, for minor welding, 52–53

Hyatt, John Wesley, 8

Inflammability, 8; of adhesives, 46; and heating, 32. See also Safety

Iron, domestic, for seams, 52, 62–63

Jig: constructing for use in welding, 54–55, 59; for holding bonded joints, 46, 49, 50; for squaring plastics, 17; for welding, 52, 53

Jigsaw, 20; bevelling with, 24; cutting foam with, 29; shaping curves with, 26

Joints: acrylic, 51; adhesives for, 46; butt, 48, 51; chart, 47; corner, 49; fasteners for, 42–43; hinging with pins, 44; right-angled, 51; sealing with filler rod, 58; with solvent, 49–50; speed welding, 61

Laminates: *layers of non-plastic materials bonded with plastic resins*; 11; aligning large surface, 97; applying 96–97; breaking with body leverage, 22; cutting, 20; cutting with circular saw, 27–28; finishing off edges, 98; interior cut on, 28; postforming grade laminate, 96; rounding curve in, 97; sealing vertical edge in, 97; making seam in, 97; sheathing 3-D objects with, 99; two cements for, 96

Laminating: fibreglass shower base, 92–93; flaws in, 94; glass fabrics for, 88–89; weatherproofing table top, 90–91

Latex: in grout and mortar, 112; in paint, 114. See also Paints

Levelling cylinder end, 16

Liquid plastics, see Resins

Marking plastic for cutting and drilling, 15; complex shapes, 19; curved lines, 18; holes to be drilled, 17; straight cut lines, 17; tubes and round rods, 18

Masonry, painting, chart, 115; preparation for painting, 116; removing stain from with acid, 117

Master: *object being duplicated in a casting*; 67; analysing shape of, 68; anchoring in frame, 68, 70; with armature, 75; in flexible moulds, 76–81; making frame for, 69; for original designs, 75; in three-part mould, 71–73

Melamine, 12; adhesives for, chart, 47

Melt-down: *melting of plastic caused by action of a power tool blade*; 20

Memory: *tendency of plastic to return to its former shape when cooling after being bent under heat*; and overbending, 32, 34

Metal, painting, chart, 115; preparation for painting, 116

Methylene dichloride (solvent): in polishing, 35, 39; in solvent cement, 46

Mitten, sheepskin, for applying paint, 119

Molecular structure of plastics, *95*

Mortar, epoxy-fortified, 112; how to use, *112*

Moulding compound: making flexible moulds with, *76–81*; types, 76. See also Moulds

Moulding plaster (plaster of Paris): handling, 69; making three-part mould with, *71–73*; making two-part mould with, *69–71*; preparing for mould-making, 68

Moulds, for liquid plastic, 67; box, 76, *80–81*; flexible, 68; one-piece surface, *76–77*; for original designs, 75; Plasticine pressed, 76, *81*; polyurethane, 76; rigid, 68, *69–70*; three-piece, *71–73*; two-part, *69–71*; two-piece shell, 76, *78–79*; types (cavities and contoured forms), 68; waste, 75; wooden, for shower base, *74–75*, *92–93*. See also Casting

Nuts and bolts, 41; sealing with patching compound, *45*

Nylon, 8, 12; drilling holes in, 30; welding, 52

Oven (domestic), heating plastic with, 32, 34

Paints, plastic-based, 101, 114; applying, 118; dipping, *120*; matching to material, chart, 115; matching old paint to be covered, chart, 116; pour-on coatings, *120*; preparing surfaces for, 116, *117*; primer coats, 114; pros and cons, box, 114; on special surfaces, *119*; spraying, *121–123*; tools for applying, chart, *118*; uses and types, 114

Parkes, Alexander, 8

Patches, 102; small unobtrusive, *103–104*; supported fibreglass, *111*; two-sided glass fibre, *109–111*; types of fillers for, 102; watertight fibreglass, 108

Patching compound, 45, *103*. See also Fillers

Patterns, paper, for cutting complex shapes, *19*; for scoop, *19*

Phenolics, 12; adhesives for, chart, 47

Pipe, plastic, bending with heat, 32; PVC, *34*

Plasticine: in flexible moulds, 76, *78–81*; for pressed mould, *81*

Plastics, blades for cutting, chart, 22; buying, 11; characteristics and varieties, 8; chart, *12–13*; cleaning, 39; in household objects, chart, *9–10*;

molecular structure of, *95*; safety rules, 8; storing, 14

Polishing, 35, *36*; an edge, *36*; inside curved surface, *37*; preparation for, 35; small-bore hole, *38*, *39*

Polishing paste, 36, 37, 38

Polycarbonate, 12; adhesives for, chart, 47; drilling holes in, 30

Polyester, 8, 12, adhesives for, chart, 47; casting from, 82; glass-reinforced, 8; filling compounds, 102; and making fibreglass, 88. See also Fillers

Polyethylene, 13; filing, 16; heat-bonding, 46; welding, 52

Polymers: *plastic molecules made up of repeated smaller molecules (monomers)*; in bending plastic, 32; pour-on plastic coatings, *120*; in sealing agents, 112

Polypropylene, 13; heat-bonding, 46; welding, 52

Polystyrene, 13; adhesives for, chart, 47; cutting, 29

Polysulphide, plastic sealant, 112; how to use, chart, 113. See also Sealants

Polyurethane, 13; adhesives for, chart, 47; cutting, 29; making moulds from, *76–81*; paint, 118; plastic sealant, 112. See also Paints, Sealants

Postforming grade laminate, *96*; shaping, 96

Potter's clay, in moulding, *75*

Pour-on coating, *101*, *120*

Primer coats, 114

Protecting plastics while cutting, 20

Protective paper: and drilling plastic, 30; and heating plastic, 32; marking for cutting plastic, 15; reusing, 14; stripping off, *14*

PVA, 13

PVC, 13; adhesives for, chart, 47; heating and bending pipe, 32, *34*; welding, 52; welding joints, *41*

PVDC, 13

Reinforced plastic: *plastic mixed with fibrous filler*; 11; cleaning, 39; cutting, 28. See also Fibreglass

Release agent: *substance that allows a plastic casting to be removed easily from its mould*; for moulds, 68, 70; polyvinyl-alcohol, 83

Repairs, household: examples of plastic for, 101. See also Fillers, Patching compound

Resin: and flaws in fibreglass, *94*; in flexible mould, *83–84*; and hardener, 82; in laminating fibreglass, *88–93*; mixing and pouring techniques, 82; and pigments, 82; and putty, 82; in rigid mould, *85–87*; repairs with fibreglass, *108–111*

Respirator: *device worn over the nose and mouth that prevents the inhalation of noxious vapours*; 8; 67

Riffler: *hand tool for shaping intricate or inaccessible surfaces*; 87

Rivet, in joinery, *42*, 43; pop rivet, *43*

Rollers, for painting, chart, 118

Round stock, see Cylinders

Router: cutting plastics with, 20; for making V-shaped groove, *26–27*; trimming laminate with, *98–99*

Safety: adhesives, 46; airless paint sprayers, box, 121; casting plastics, 67, 82; general rules, 8; heating plastic, 32; laminating fibreglass, 89, 108; plastic fillers, box, 102; power tools, 20; preparing surfaces for paint, 117; welding, 56

Sanding, to finish inside curved surface, *36*; to remove scratches, *38*; sandpaper chart, 35; wet, *36*

Saw: contouring with, *25*; cutting plastic with, 20; forming bevelled edge with, *24*; forming curves with, *26*; interior cut with, *28*; saw blade types, chart, 22; sawing tubes and rods, *24*, *25*. See also Band saw, Circular saw, Jigsaw

Scoring tool, 20, *21*

Scraping, to finish off, 35, *36*

Scratches: avoiding during cleaning, 39; protection from when heating plastic, 32; removing from acrylic sheet, *38*; removing with toothpaste, 35

Screws; heated, for thermoplastic threads, 44; types for joinery, *42*

Sealants, plastic: caulking, *113*; types and usage, *112*, chart, 113

Seams in plastic film, *62–63*

Shaping: acrylic into irregular shapes, *34*; curves with jigsaw, *26*; foam, 29; heated plastic with forming blocks, 32, *33*; heated PVC pipe, *34*

Sheet, plastic: bending, *33*, 34; breaking with body leverage, 22; cutting with band saw, *23*; drilling holes in, *31*; heating to shape, 32; marking cut lines on, *17*, *18*; removing scratch from, *38*; ridding of static electricity, 117; scoring and snapping, 20, *21*; squaring edges and corners in, *17*; testing for squareness, 15, *16*

Sheet-metal, repairing dent in, *106–107*

Shower base, laminated, *92–93*; making mould for, *74–75*

Shrinkage, in mould casting, 82

Shrink tubing, 62, *65*

Shrink-wrapping: *enclosing an object in a plastic wrapping*; 62, *64–65*

Silicones, 13. *See also* Paints, Sealants
Solvent cementing: *melting plastics chemically to join them*; 8, 41, 56; for filling corner joint, *49*; dip, *49–50*; mistakes to avoid when using, *50*; softening edges with, *48*; water test before cementing, 47
Spraying, paint: with airless gun, *121*; on horizontal surfaces, *123*; preparing paint for, *122*; safety and box, 121, 122; setting up area for, *122*; on walls, 123
Sprue hole: *hole in a mould through which the casting material is poured*; 68, *84*
Squareness, testing for: rods and tubes, *15*; sheets, *16*
Squaring edges and corners, *17*
Static electricity, ridding sheet plastic of, *117*
Storing plastic stock, *14*
Structural foam, 11
Synthetic rubber, 13. *See also* Paint

Table saw, *see* Saw
Tapping tool: *tool for cutting screw threads in a hole*; *107*

Tap wrench, *45*
Thermoplastics, 8; cleaning, 39; drill bits for, *30*; forming threads with heated screw, *44*; hems and seams in, *62–63*; polishing drilled holes in, *35*; shrink-wrapping and tubing, *64–65*; welding joints in, *52–61*
Thermosetting plastics, 8; adhesives for, chart, 47; cleaning, 39
Threads: cutting new, *107*; making with heated screw, *44*; renewing with plastic filler, *107*
Tools: for cutting foam, 29; for cutting plastic, 20; for drilling, 30; for laminating fibreglass, 89; for painting, chart, 118, *119*; for sanding and polishing, 35
Try square, *15*, 16

V-groove: when bending heated plastic, 32; cutting, *26–27*; polishing sides of, 35; repairing crack with, *106*
V-joint, welding, *41*
V-shaped jig, marking plastic in, 15, *18*
Vice, use in welding, *55*

Vinyl paint: covering old paint, chart, 116; pros and cons, box, 114; usage, chart, 115. *See also* Paints

Waterproofing outdoor table with fibreglass, *90–91*
Wax: paraffin wax, in patching, *103*; polishing, 35; wax paste, 35, 37, 38
Welding: *joining plastics by heating and fusing edges*; butt weld, 57; constructing jig for use in, *54–55*; corner weld, *57*; with hotplate, *52–53*; overlap weld, *57*; patching holes, *60*; PVC joints, *41*; with scrap metal, *53–54, 55*; sealing butt joint, *58*; speed-welding, *61*; thermoplastics, *52–61*; T-weld, *59*
Welding torch: and fashioning seams, 62; nozzles for, *57*; and shrink-wrapping, 62, *64–65*; speed-welding tip, *61*; use, 56, *58–59*
Wood: bits, modifying for drilling plastic, *31*; painting, chart, 115; patching with plastic filler, 102; preparing surface for paint, 116; wood screw, thermoplastic threads for, *44*; wood-working vice, *16*

Metric Conversion Chart

Approximate equivalents—length

Millimetres to inches		Inches to millimetres	
1	1/32	1/32	1
2	1/16	1/16	2
3	1/8	1/8	3
4	5/32	3/16	5
5	3/16	1/4	6
6	1/4	5/16	8
7	9/32	3/8	10
8	5/16	7/16	11
9	11/32	1/2	13
10 (1cm)	3/8	9/16	14
11	7/16	5/8	16
12	15/32	11/16	17
13	1/2	3/4	19
14	9/16	13/16	21
15	19/32	7/8	22
16	5/8	15/16	24
17	11/16	1	25
18	23/32	2	51
19	3/4	3	76
20	25/32	4	102
25	1	5	127
30	1 3/16	6	152
40	1 9/16	7	178
50	1 31/32	8	203
60	2 3/8	9	229
70	2 3/4	10	254
80	3 5/32	11	279
90	3 9/16	12 (1ft)	305
100	3 15/16	13	330
200	7 7/8	14	356
300	11 13/16	15	381
400	15 3/4	16	406
500	19 11/16	17	432
600	23 5/8	18	457
700	27 9/16	19	483
800	31 1/2	20	508
900	35 7/16	24 (2ft)	610
1000 (1m)	39 3/8		

Metres to feet/inches		Yards to metres	
		1	0.914
2	6′ 7″	2	1.83
3	9′ 10″	3	2.74
4	13′ 1″	4	3.66
5	16′ 5″	5	4.57
6	19′ 8″	6	5.49
7	23′ 0″	7	6.40
8	26′ 3″	8	7.32
9	29′ 6″	9	8.23
10	32′ 10″	10	9.14
20	65′ 7″	20	18.29
50	164′ 0″	50	45.72
100	328′ 1″	100	91.44

Conversion factors

Length

1 millimetre (mm)	= 0.0394 in
1 centimetre (cm)/10 mm	= 0.3937 in
1 metre/100 cm	= 39.37 in/3.281 ft/1.094 yd
1 kilometre (km)/1000 metres	= 1093.6 yd/0.6214 mile
1 inch (in)	= 25.4 mm/2.54 cm
1 foot (ft)/12 in	= 304.8 mm/30.48 cm/0.3048 metre
1 yard (yd)/3 ft	= 914.4 mm/91.44 cm/0.9144 metre
1 mile/1760 yd	= 1609.344 metres/1.609 km

Area

1 square centimetre (sq cm)/ 100 square millimetres (sq mm)	= 0.155 sq in
1 square metre (sq metre)/10,000 sq cm	= 10.764 sq ft/1.196 sq yd
1 are/100 sq metres	= 119.60 sq yd/0.0247 acre
1 hectare (ha)/100 ares	= 2.471 acres/0.00386 sq mile
1 square inch (sq in)	= 645.16 sq mm/6.4516 sq cm
1 square foot (sq ft)/144 sq in	= 929.03 sq cm
1 square yard (sq yd)/9 sq ft	= 8361.3 sq cm/0.8361 sq metre
1 acre/4840 sq yd	= 4046.9 sq metres/0.4047 ha
1 square mile/640 acres	= 259 ha/2.59 sq km

Volume

1 cubic centimetre (cu cm)/ 1000 cubic millimetres (cu mm)	= 0.0610 cu in
1 cubic decimetre (cu dm)/1000 cu cm	= 61.024 cu in/0.0353 cu ft
1 cubic metre/1000 cu dm	= 35.3147 cu ft/1.308 cu yd
1 cu cm	= 1 millilitre (ml)
1 cu dm	= 1 litre see **Capacity**
1 cubic inch (cu in)	= 16.3871 cu cm
1 cubic foot (cu ft)/1728 cu in	= 28,316.8 cu cm/0·0283 cu metre
1 cubic yard (cu yd)/27 cu ft	= 0.7646 cu metre

Capacity

1 litre	= 1.7598 pt/0.8799 qt/0.22 gal
1 pint (pt)	= 0.568 litre
1 quart (qt)	= 1.137 litres
1 gallon (gal)	= 4.546 litres

Weight

1 gram (g)	= 0.035 oz
1 kilogram (kg)/1000 g	= 2.20 lb/35.2 oz
1 tonne/1000 kg	= 2204.6 lb/0.9842 ton
1 ounce (oz)	= 28.35 g
1 pound (lb)	= 0.4536 kg
1 ton	= 1016 kg

Pressure

1 gram per square metre (g/metre^2)	= 0.0295 oz/sq yd
1 gram per square centimetre (g/cm^2)	= 0.228 oz/sq in
1 kilogram per square centimetre (kg/cm^2)	= 14.223 lb/sq in
1 kilogram per square metre (kg/metre^2)	= 0.205 lb/sq ft
1 pound per square foot (lb/ft^2)	= 4.882 kg/metre^2
1 pound per square inch (lb/in^2)	= 703.07 kg/metre^2
1 ounce per square yard (oz/yd^2)	= 33.91 g/metre^2
1 ounce per square foot (oz/ft^2)	= 305.15 g/metre^2

Temperature

To convert °F to °C, subtract 32, then divide by 9 and multiply by 5

To convert °C to °F, divide by 5 and multiply by 9, then add 32

Phototypeset by Tradespools Limited, Frome, Somerset
Colour reproduction by Grafascan Limited, Dublin, Ireland
Printed and bound by Artes Gráficas Toledo, SA, Spain

D. L. TO:1192 -1987